Crisis Care ™

Hope for the Hurting

With Dr. H. Norman Wright

Along with

Dr. Steve Arterburn
Dr. Carl Brecheen
Dr. Paul Faulkner

Dr. Gene and Elaine Getz
Dr. Howard Hendricks
Dr. E.V. Hill
Dr. Frank Minirth

Dr. Gary Oliver
Dennis Rainey
Dr. John Trent

Workbook Written by
Mark W. Presley with H. Norman Wright

Workbook Editor
Jamie Jewell

Producer
Greg Vaughn

Director/Editor
Fred Holmes

Associate Producers
Scott Peck **David Hicks**

Grace Products Corporation
1761 International Parkway, Suite 135
Richardson, Texas 75081
Phone: 1-800-527-4014

Scripture quotations are from the
King James Version of the Holy Bible.

Published by
Grace Products Corporation
1761 International Parkway, Suite 135
Richardson, TX   75081

**For additional information or workbooks,
dial 1-800-527-4014**

Contents

Dear Friends;

You may be a parent, a church deacon or elder, a school teacher, or an active lay person. This video series is for you! you may be a Pastor, a concerned Christian, a prayer partner, or a seminary student. This series is for you! You may be a professional counselor with a doctorate, a Bible study leader, a youth worker, an active church member. This series is for you!

This video curriculum represents a dream come true. Over the years, I have discovered that we can all learn to minister and help those that are in the mist of crisis. "Crisis Care" has come into existence to train you to do

just that. There are hurting people all around us. There has been a death in the family. What do you say? What do you do? Maybe someone has lost their job. How can you help? How can you make a difference? Or, what if someone has just been told their spouse is divorcing them. What should you tell them? How can you minister to their needs?

Crisis is part of each and every person's life. God has called us to minister to one another. Christ has commanded us to "love one another even as I have loved you" John 13:34. "Crisis Care" will teach you how to do just that. You will be grounded in counseling basics. Then, you'll have an opportunity to apply what you have learned by going through various case studies. We can make a difference and help those who are in pain and those who are hurting!

Yours Truly in Christ,

H. Norman Wright

DR H. NORMAN WRIGHT is one of America's best known Christian counselors. He is founder and director of Christian Marriage Enrichment, and is in private practice as a marriage and family counselor at Family Counseling and Enrichment in Tustin, California.

Dr. Wright has served on the faculty of Talbot Theological Seminary and is author of more than 55 books, including *Quiet Times for Couples, Communication: Key to Your Marriage* and the number one best-seller, *Always Daddy's Girl*. Norm and his wife Joyce, live in southern California, and have been married for more than 40 years.

SESSION I

"People in Pain"

 **Notes**

People in Pain

Crisis and Loss

> May the Father of all mercies . . .
> comfort us in all our tribulations, that we may be able
> to comfort them which are in ANY trouble.
> 2 Corinthians 1:3-4 (KJV)

When crisis comes to our lives—or to those around us—what's the right thing to say, the right thing to do? Sometimes we're lucky and we have just the right words, but often it's wrong, wrong, wrong. What are the guidelines for saying and doing the right things?

The unique series you are beginning is designed to give guidelines on how to help others, as well as yourself, in dealing with crises. *Crisis Care* as a title says it all. The objective of this series is for you to become a person who can care when others are hurting.

This won't make you a professional counselor—that takes extensive training and experience—but you will have tools to be a caring friend, a loving church member, and a sympathetic ear, which is where the healing in crises should begin.

The professionals can only do so much. People need friends, and friends need to know what to say.

Viewing the Video

What is a Crisis?

Ask any group of individuals: "Have you had a crisis in your life?" Heads will nod knowingly; eyes may glaze over. But ask for examples and you'll have wide variation. Some appear to make tragedies from the simplest of things; yet others have problems so severe that one can't imagine how they could cope.

Are all of these crises? Actually, we have the freedom to decide what's a crisis for us; however, there are some guidelines that Dr. Wright develops in this session. He distinguishes between a crisis and a loss. Both are important and must be dealt with, but the crisis is particularly severe.

How Do People Respond in a Crisis?

When people go through a crisis or a loss, they tend to do one of two things:

- **Withdraw** because they don't know what to say
- They **talk too much**

In a crisis, people want to help. Their hearts are in the right spot, but they don't know how. This series teaches us what to say, what to do, and how to give comfort and support to hurting individuals.

The Purpose of this Series

The purpose is to equip every individual in a church to:

- Be better able to **understand loss and crisis**.
- **Know what to say** to those in crisis.

Life is full of losses and crises. There is a basic framework of ways to minister to people during these crises.

> *"As a pastor, I need the body of Christ.*
> *In fact there are people in my congregation who can*
> *meet the needs of people in a way that I can't . . ."*
>
> *Dr. Gene Getz*

Examples of Crises

Check (√) if this type of loss has touched your life.

- ☐ Loss of a job
- ☐ Loss of a friend
- ☐ Loss of status
- ☐ Incapacitating illness/operation
- ☐ Death of a family member
- ☐ Terminal illness
- ☐ Individuals on drugs

- ☐ Discovery of homosexuality
- ☐ Discovering a disability
- ☐ Abortion or unwanted pregnancy
- ☐ Natural disasters—hurricanes, etc.
- ☐ Suicide attempt
- ☐ Separation or divorce
- ☐ Child custody battles

- ☐ Being drafted or discharged
- ☐ Spiritual conflicts in families
- ☐ Miscarriage or premature birth
- ☐ Parents go to a home for the aged
- ☐ Mid-life crisis
- ☐ Life with a depressed person
- ☐ The discovery of Alzheimer's

- ☐ Heart attacks
- ☐ _____
- ☐ _____
- ☐ _____
- ☐ _____
- ☐ _____
- ☐ _____

> *"What we have to do is go beyond ourselves and remember the fact that God loves us and has a plan."*
>
> *Dr. Steve Arterburn*

 STOP **Group Discussion**

Stop the video at the point indicated by Dr. Wright and answer the following questions.

✎ What was the most recent crisis that you've experienced in your life personally?

_____

_____

_____

Why did you call it a crisis?

_____

_____

_____

_____

_____

_____

Take time to discuss this in your groups.

Grace Products

Loss vs. Crisis

There is a difference between a loss and a crisis.

> ✎ A loss really _____ and is part of a crisis.
>
> A crisis _____ a person.

Characteristics of a Crisis

A crisis can be any number of things:
- A crucial time
- A turning point
- A time of change
- A time of despair but also of opportunity
- A pivotal point in any person's life

However, a basic overall definition of a crisis is . . .

> ✎ A state in which people have failed to_____.

Symptoms of a Crisis

People in crisis exhibit any number of the following symptoms:
- They're in **disequilibrium**
- They show signs of **stress**
- There is an **attitude of panic or defeat**
- **Decreased efficiency**
- **Focused on relief**

Questions and Answers

Review

1. What is a crisis?

2. What is a loss?

3. What is the purpose of this series?

Loss vs. Crisis

In the following situations decide whether it would be a loss or a crisis for you. Tell what you would say to another person who had the problem.

1. They have cut 500 employees, and Bob got his notice this morning. This won't be the end of it, and I may go next.
   A. crisis   B. loss
   What do you say? _____.

2. She's been a best friend for the past 5 years. I depend on a friend like her, but after last night's argument, I don't think she'll talk to me again.
   A. crisis   B. loss
   What do you say? _____.

3. Dad's gone. When cancer takes that long, you die a little each day watching him go, and you almost want it to end.
   A. crisis   B. loss
   What do you say? _____.

4. Oh, no! Amy didn't make cheerleader.
   A. crisis   B. loss
   What do you say? _____.

5. He asked me to leave. I took the children and we're at mother's. John is talking to him right now, but he's drinking again, so I don't know.
   A. crisis   B. loss
   What do you say? _____.

6. It was his favorite car, but I'm thankful that he wasn't hurt in the accident.

   A. crisis   B. loss

   What do you say? _____.

7. The engagement is over. I'm glad it's over. I've tried and tried to get him to change, but nothing seems to work.

   A. crisis   B. loss

   What do you say? _____.

8. I asked her out to dinner, but she said no.

   A. crisis   B. loss

   What do you say? _____.

9. It's so hard seeing my mother lose her health like that. Yesterday she couldn't even remember my name—my own mother! I cried and cried.

   A. crisis   B. loss

   What do you say? _____.

10. I love the new colors in the kid's bedroom; but Johnny has already used this black marker, and there's a pizza stain on the desk that won't wash.

    A. crisis   B. loss

    What do you say? _____.

Personal Applications

1. Rate yourself on your own ability to deal with individuals in crisis.

Poor				Good
1	2	3	4	5

2. In what areas do you excel in dealing with others?

3. Describe one crisis that has taught you a life lesson.

4. Describe one crisis in which you should have learned something but did not.

5. Do you see a crisis surfacing around you now?

6. Are you predictable in the way you respond to a crisis?

7. Describe a crisis in which you didn't respond predictably.

Dealing With Crisis in Your Church

A key objective in this series is to develop crisis care in church groups. Consider the following questions about your church.

	Poor				Good
	1	2	3	4	5

1. Rate your church or organization on its ability to deal with individuals in crisis.

2. What could your church do to improve ministry in this area?

3. What can you do to help your church?

Goals and Prayers

1. Write some personal goals for yourself for this *Crisis Care* series—specific areas where you want to improve your skills, goals for your church's ministry, etc.

   _____.

   _____.

   _____.

   _____.

   _____.

2. Write your prayer list for this session and for the coming week.

   _____.

   _____.

   _____.

   _____.

   _____.

   _____.

   _____.

   _____.

3. A suggested Bible passage for the week is Job 4:1-5:27. This is the account of Job and the counsel of three of his friends during a time of crisis. What observations and applications can you find? What is God's answer to Job?

_____ .

_____ .

_____ .

_____ .

SESSION II

"Bridges Over Troubled Water"

 **Notes**

Bridges Over Troubled Water

Characteristics of a Crisis

God is our refuge and strength,
a very present help in trouble.
Psalm 46:1 (KJV)

A crisis has telltale signs—actions and behavior that happen in predictable ways. In this session, we will begin to learn some of these signs and some initial responses for care givers.

It's important at the start to categorize the crisis. One way is to recognize the root causes. Are they from exhaustion or from a sudden shocking event?

It's important to recognize how people respond to a crisis. Some see a crisis as a threat, others see it as a loss, many see it as a challenge—a time for growth, a time to learn more about God. Learn to recognize people's responses so that you can respond as a care giver.

It's important to plan for our initial response to those in crisis. When a crisis hits a friend, we are not the ones to tell them what to do. We are to be listeners. We are not there to offer immediate solutions. We are there as a friend. Eventually, they'll have to find solutions for themselves. But in the beginning, they are still in the severe part of the crisis and may be having a flood of emotions.

Viewing the Video

Characteristics of a Crisis

1. *Most crises hit* _____ .

2. *Others can be* _____ .

    Anticipatory crises:
    - "Type A" personalities
    - Male mid-life crises

Men who go through mid-life crises:
- Don't share emotions or feelings
- Have no close male friendships
- Their identity is in their work

3. *It threatens your_____.*

The resolution of a crisis is **uncertain**. We are not in control. This is an opportunity to **depend on God** more—to learn to live by faith.

> *"Frequently God allows problems to come into our life that throw us back on Him, so that we come to understand: my need is not partial, it's total."*
>
> *Dr. Howard Hendricks*

Do Not Tell Them What to Do

1. *You are not the one to tell them exactly what to do.*

   Listen to them. Don't offer solutions at this time. Just be a friend. They will eventually have to find a solution for themselves, but at this time they are still in the intense part of the crisis and are experiencing a rush of feelings.

   A crisis presents dilemmas.
   > *"What should I do?"*
   > *"Is this the best way to go?"*
   > *"Is this the right decision they will make?"*

   You don't tell them what to do because you **make them dependent** on you, and you **lower their self-esteem** even more. People in crisis need to gain the strength of determining their own solutions.

 STOP **Group Discussion**

Stop the video at the point indicated by Dr. Wright and answer the following questions.

✐ How do men and women handle crises differently?

_____

_____

_____

Take time to discuss this in your groups.

_____

2. *A crisis helps us define our values.*

> "Crises are the times when I really can grow the most in my spiritual and emotional life, if I allow those crises to become a part of my life in such a way that I will look to the Lord and trust Him more to work things out . . ."
>
> *Elaine Getz*

Crisis Overview

A crisis commonly develops because of either some catastrophe or a series of smaller events

1. *The exhaustion crisis*
    An individual can cope effectively for some period of time, but eventually the individual is **just worn out**.

2. *The shock crisis*
    A major event is so big and so serious that the individual **feels overwhelmed**. The event puts the person out of balance—they feel vulnerable. The tension builds and then one little event plunges them into a crisis.

> "You are an eternal being.
> You have an eternal God and He has pastors
> and believers to help you over this crisis.
> Your problem is you believe you're unique;
> you believe you're the only one who's had the problem.
> Come on out and see the millions who have overcome!"
>
> *Dr. E.V. Hill*

How People Interpret Crises

1. *As a* _____.
    A great deal of anxiety is involved.

2. *As a* _____.
    There is a sense of depression, deprivation or mourning.

3. *As a* _____.
    There is a heightened sense of anxiety—but with a kindling of hope. Challenges are realistic struggles in a person's life, but they may activate other conflicts that have not been resolved.

The Intense Part of a Crisis

There is a set of predictable phases in a crisis. These are covered in a later session, For now, understand that there is an initial intense part of a crisis.

1. *The intense crisis period lasts . . .*

    . . . 4 to 6 weeks.

2. *We should help the person in crisis during this time because they are . . .*

    . . . open to help and responsive.

3. *If we let it go on and they don't get help this time . . .*

    . . . They may reach out to things that do not help—alcohol, drugs, etc.

During this time the individual is reintegrating his or her life. He/she will find new ways to cope with problems.

> *All of us can learn to minister to others*
> *during this time of crisis.*

Questions and Answers

Review

1. How do crises develop—suddenly or slowly?

2. How should you respond when individuals in crisis ask you what to do?

3. How do people react to an exhaustion crisis? To a shock crisis?

4. How should we respond during the intense part of a crisis? For how long?

5. What can happen if we don't respond to individuals during the intense part of a crisis?

Depending on God

An important emphasis in this lesson was that crises bring us closer to God.

1. How is a crisis an opportunity to depend on God?

2. Describe a crisis in which God has helped you. Did you feel closer to God at the end?

3. Describe a crisis in which you were separate from God. What could have been done to bring God into the solution?

Situations—What Do I Do?

In each of the following situations, how do you react? Remember that: "You are not the one to tell them what to do."

1. What do I do? I've been working for that company for 20 years. I don't have any other skills. There were 20 of us given notice this morning.

    What do you say to this person? _____.

    _____.

2. If he does recover, he'll be totally paralyzed. He's comatose and may never gain consciousness. The doctor says to take him off life support. I don't know what to do! What do you think I should do?

    What do you say? _____ .

    _____ .

3. Mary has wanted to be on the dance squad since she was a little girl, but she just doesn't have the ability. As her mother, I don't want to set her up for failure. What do you think?

    What do you say to Mary's mother? _____ .

    _____ .

4. It's a great job opportunity, but I wish it hadn't come right now. The company I'm with is just about to turn the corner. I feel so responsible for what happens. Every time there has been a crisis, I'm the one who has had to be there to bail them out.

    What do you say to this person? _____ .

    _____ .

5. I know her murder has crushed you emotionally, and it's hard to clean up your sister's personal stuff, but trust me, it's better just to get rid of it. Sell the jewelry and take the clothes to the shelter. Most of that stuff is junk anyway; I'm sure you'll end up throwing most of it away. Believe me, if you clear it out it helps the healing process.

    What do you think of this advice? _____ .

    _____ .

Threat, Loss or Challenge

In each of the following situations, is the individual responding to the crisis as a loss, threat, or challenge?

1. A high school junior has to move with her family to a another state and spend her senior year at a new school.

2. A man in his fifties loses his job.

3. A family has to move to a smaller house because of a loss of income.

4. Your team just lost the championship game.

5. A person discovers that his/her spouse had an affair years ago.

6. A man retires after 35 years with the same company. He has developed no outside interests and his work has been his life.

7. An earthquake destroys your home.

8. The doctor tells you that you have cancer.

9. To prevent a miscarriage, you must sell your business and spend most of the next 6 months in bed.

Personal Applications

1. Have you ever told a person what to do in a crisis and later regretted it? Explain.

2. When a crisis happens to you, do you tend to interpret it as a loss, a threat or a challenge?

3. Describe one crisis from your experience that you would characterize as a **shock crisis**. Describe one that you would characterize as an **exhaustion crisis**.

4. Have you ever experienced the intense part of a crisis? What was going through your mind at that time?

5. When you had this intense crisis experience, how did you want people to behave around you?

Summary and Prayers

1. What have you learned from this lesson?

_____.

_____.

_____.

_____.

_____.

2. Write your prayer list for this session and for the coming week.

_____ .

_____ .

_____ .

_____ .

_____ .

_____ .

_____ .

SESSION III

"Trusting God"

 **Notes**

Session 3

Trusting God

Counseling Fundamentals: Part 1

> Trust in the Lord with all thine heart;
> and lean not unto thine own understanding.
> Proverbs 3:5 (KJV)

To counsel, we need to learn some principles based on Scripture. This is a return to the basics. The goal is to provide you with fundamentals so you won't make fundamental mistakes. Dr. Wright discusses eight fundamentals in this session. You'll want to memorize them and practice them in your own day-to-day situations.

These are Biblical principles. As a part of crisis care, it's very important to rely on God—to be in prayer and to rely on Christian attitudes, Christian love, and Christian hope.

In the questions at the end of this session there is special emphasis put on listening, the first fundamental, and probably the most important. If we can do nothing else in crisis care, we can be good listeners.

Viewing the Video

Principles for Counseling

Principles for Counseling 1-8 are discussed in this session. In Session 5, the discussion will continue with additional principles.

1. Listening

Counseling is knowing when to speak and when to stay silent.

> *He that answereth a matter before he heareth it,*
> *it is folly and shame unto him.*
> *Proverbs 18:13 (KJV)*

> *Wherefore my beloved brethren,*
> *let every man be swift to hear,*
> *slow to speak, slow to wrath.*
> *James 1:19 (KJV)*

A **definition of Listening**. When the other person is talking, you're not thinking about what you will say when they quit talking.

✎ The ears are not necessarily **the main organ of listening**. What is important?

_____

In listening, 65% of the message comes from non-verbal communication, so watch for body language.

> *"The main thing people need is someone who will*
> *listen to them with a sympathetic ear and will be*
> *supportive of them in times of real difficulty."*
>
> *Dr. Carl Brecheen*

2. Rely on the Power of God

Often when we counsel, we don't know what to say. In these situations, rely on the power of God. Being open to God's guidance is the key for knowing how and when to counsel.

> *Trust in the Lord with all thine heart*
> *and lean not onto thine own understanding. In all thy ways*
> *acknowledge Him, and He shall direct thy paths.*
> *Proverbs 3:5-6 (KJV)*

When you don't know where to go or what to do, pray silently:
"Lord give me insight and guidance right now, please."

3. Maintain Genuine Interest and Love

If you are not fully interested in the person, and if you don't really care for him, he's going to pick it up. If you have a personality issue or conflict with the individual you are counseling, it could come across.

There might be occasions where it would be better for you to say:

"From what you're sharing with me, I think there may be someone else who could minister to you at this time."

4. Know When to Speak and When to be Quiet

Timing is everything when it comes to speaking and listening.

> *"We don't know why things happen.*
> *God alone knows why things happen."*
>
> *Dr. Carl Brecheen*

Group Discussion

✎ Practically speaking, how do you encourage someone?

_____

_____

> *In the multitude of words there wanteth not sin;*
> *but he that refraineth his lips is wise.*
> *Proverbs 10:19 (KJV)*
>
> *He that hath knowledge spareth his words; and a man of*
> *understanding is of an excellent spirit. Even a fool,*
> *when he holdeth his peace, is counted wise; and he that*
> *shutteth his lips is esteemed a man of understanding.*
> *Proverbs 17:27-28 (KJV)*

> *The heart of the wise teacheth his mouth,*
> *and addeth learning to his lips. Pleasant words are as an*
> *honeycomb, sweet to the soul, and health to the bones.*
> *Proverbs 16:23-24 (KJV)*

Advice for **extroverts**—Keep a lid on it! Control yourself. Do not interrupt or give answers. Instead, relax and take things in. Pleasant words heal, so use them.

> *A Model for Honest Caring:*
>
> *"I don't know how you feel—I've never been there—*
> *but I want you to know I care, I love you, I care."*
>
> *Dr. Gene Getz*

5. Keep Confidences

Be a trusted person. Do not violate the trust of what has been shared with you.

✎ What should we do about sharing prayer requests for the person in crisis?

_____

What about sharing with your spouse?_____.

If you feel the need to share a person's need with others such as prayer groups or prayer chains, **ask that person for permission**.

6. Saying the Right Words and Giving Advice

The best way to give advice is to give choices. You can say:

"You know, I have three different ideas. What do you think about these?"

Then let them select the piece of advice that would work best. Individuals need ownership of their decisions. Give them choices and then let them make the final selection.

7. Helping and Edifying

We are called to build up individuals—not to tear them down.

✏ To edify means to_____.

As you minister to a person in a crisis, you might need to loan them your faith and your hope.

The individual with whom you are counseling may not have the faith and hope to carry on, but you can provide them with the strength from your faith and hope. Give the other person courage. Build him/her up. Be a cheerleader. A person who really listens to feelings is a valuable friend in a time of crisis.

8. Be Involved and Empathic

Empathy means that you **feel with the other person**. You are able to walk in his/her shoes. Being empathic means you are with them intellectually and emotionally at the time of counseling, but then you relinquish that attachment when that person is not there.

✏ How do you relinquish empathy from a counseling session?

_____

Praying for the individual . . .
- Reminds us that God does the ministering.
- Brings that person before God.
- Helps you remember the person's name and their problems.

However, be careful about being too empathic. It can drain you into completely assuming the other person's burden.

> *You are not there to solve their problems—*
> *just to guide and to love them.*

Questions and Answers

Review

Memorize each of the following Counseling Fundamentals.
1. *Learn to Listen*
2. *Rely on the power of God*
3. *Maintain genuine interest and love*
4. *Know when to speak and when to be quiet*
5. *Keep confidences*
6. *Be very careful when giving advice.*
7. *Help and edify*
8. *Be involved with the person and empathic*

A Practice Journal

During the coming week, use these fundamentals in your own interactions with other people. These do not need be crisis care situations. The principles discussed by Dr. Wright are also good for many day-to-day relationships. The objective here is to put principles into practice in simple situations, so they'll be available in the crisis situations.

Keep a journal of specific incidents in which you used one of the fundamentals. Give a date and a brief note for each incident.

For example, in a business situation where you do not have answers, you rely on God for an answer and it comes. Write in your journal the date and a few words to remember the incident later.

Guided Listening

Guided listening means active participation with the speaker by probing the speaker's thoughts with questions. The questions: (1) often simply reflect back what the speaker is saying and (2) are open-ended—they invite more than a yes or no type of answer. The goal is to have the person discover new things about himself/herself, about relationships, and about personal problems; but in particular, to discover these things through self revelation.

For example:

Speaker—*Everyone at the office hates me!*

Listener—*Everyone hates you?*

Speaker—*Well, not everyone. It's mainly John and Mary. They're always rude to me.*

Listener—*Oh. What do you mean when you say they're always rude?*

Speaker—*Well, you know. Yesterday, John started telling me how I ought to rearrange some of the sections on that report.*

Listener—*Was he angry or did he have some good suggestions?*

Speaker—*Well, what he told me was okay, but it was just the way he said it.*

Listener—*Oh. How did he say it?*

Speaker—*He never smiles when he talks to me. It's like he has a lot of trouble talking to me. Why can't he just be natural?*

Listener—*Why would he have a lot of trouble talking to you?*

Break into pairs and practice guided listening with each of the following situations posed by a speaker. One person takes the part of the listener and the other takes the part of the speaker with a problem. The person with the problem needs to be creative; the listener needs to ask guided questions. Switch partners after each situation.

1. I keep getting asked to do all this volunteer work and it's too much. I wish people would stop asking me.

2. He asked me to take on the new position of department head, but I know I'm not ready.

3. I just can't decide on a name for the baby.

4. If I find the man who did this, I'll kill him.

5. She wants to get serious, but I'm just not ready for the responsibility.

6. He wants to marry me eventually, but now is just not the right time for him.

7. I'm ashamed of how I talk.

Factors that Affect Listening

Share in your groups your ideas about how each of the following affect the skill of listening. This is adapted from *Crisis Counseling*, by H. Norman Wright.

1. *Gender*   Men vs. women

3.	*Education*	High school vs. college trained Professional counselor vs. untrained
4.	*Past experience*	A life of personal difficulties vs. a life of relative ease
5.	*Attitude*	Optimistic vs. pessimistic
6.	*Personal feelings*	A listener's personal feelings about the person talking
7.	*Emotional/ physical state*	Too tired/alert, too sick/healthy, too stressed/in control

Biblical Principles for Listening

Check the following Biblical references for insights on good listening.

1. Proverbs 17:27-28 _____.

2. Proverbs 11:3 _____.

3. 1 Corinthians 2:1-5 _____.

4. Proverbs 25:20 _____.

5. 1 Thessalonians 5:11 _____.

Respond to each of the following statements in order to teach others how to help those in crises to rely more on God.

1. I want to pray with the person but maybe he'll take it wrong.

2. She's blaming God for the problem.

3. We talked all night and I didn't even think to pray, even to myself. I'm praying now, but I don't think God will honor what's been said.

4. He kept wanting to talk about God. It was okay at first, but he just kept talking and talking. One moment he was blaming God: the next he was praising Him.

5. Don't worry about anything. God's in charge. I don't care how bad you feel, if you just rely on God, everything is just going to be okay.

5. Don't worry about anything. God's in charge. I don't care how bad you feel, if you just rely on God, everything is just going to be okay.

Personal Applications

Rate yourself on how well you apply some of the fundamentals in your daily life.

		Poor				Well
1.	How well do you listen?	1	2	3	4	5
2.	How well do you rely on the power of God?	1	2	3	4	5
3.	How well do you show genuine interest and love?	1	2	3	4	5
4.	How well do you know when to be quiet?	1	2	3	4	5
5.	How well do you keep confidences?	1	2	3	4	5
6.	How well do you feel empathy?	1	2	3	4	5

7. List the two areas in which you need the most improvement.

_____.

Summary and Prayers

1. What have you learned from this lesson?

_____.

_____.

2. Write your prayer list for this session and for the coming week.

_____.

_____.

_____.

_____.

_____.

✎ Notes

SESSION IV

"Heavenly Perspective"

✎ Notes

Heavenly Perspective

Counseling Fundamentals: Part 2

> Look not every man on his own things,
> but every man also on the things of others.
> Philippians 2:4 (KJV)

Part two of Counseling Fundamentals covers the very difficult topic of admonishing and teaching. Sometimes in our dealings with others we have to say some difficult things. Our primary function is to listen and to encourage, but there is always the time when we have to say something the person may not want to hear. To do this it's important to be gentle and careful.

Also Dr. Wright discusses honesty, which is always an important factor, and acceptance. Sometimes we may hear things that shock us, but as Dr. Wright says, we need to keep control of our feelings and judgment.

These skills are particularly important in the first phase of a crisis—the Impact Phase—which requires great care and considerable patience. Dr. Wright closes out this session with a discussion of this phase.

Viewing the Video

Principles for Counseling (Continued)

Principles for Counseling 1-8 were discussed in Session 3. We continue here with Principle 9.

9. Teaching and Admonishing

✐ Another word that goes along with admonishing is . . .

You can say many difficult things if you have . . .
- The proper attitude
- The proper tone of voice

- A gentle spirit

Be **tentative** in your approach: "Could it be that this might be something you're doing that you're not even aware of? Have you ever considered that . . .?"

Admonishing often means to tell a person what is right and wrong—to tell them something they don't want to hear—but when you do this, include **gentleness**.

✐ You never confront (admonish) until you've built a . . .

_____

The person needs to understand your care and concern for them before you can be effective in admonitions. This means time in listening, getting to know them, and showing your honest concern.

> "For a person who is depressed, one of the tendencies is to withdraw from the people who can really help you the most. When I get discouraged, it's very important to find a friend. . . For me to express to them how I'm feeling."
>
> Dennis Rainey

Group Discussion

Stop the video at the point indicated and answer the following question.

✐ What are the spiritual truths you've learned as a result of the crises in your life?

_____

_____

_____

10. Be honest

Be honest about **who you are as a person**—being transparent.
- Be honest in **answering questions**.
- Be honest about your **failings**.

If you recommend a certain behavior, can the person you are counseling ask if the behavior applies to you?

_____

11. Be accepting

People you counsel need to feel

_____

You may hear about sin. You may be shocked about what you hear, but do not overreact.

You need to keep control of your feelings, emotions and judgment.

> *"We need to resist the temptation to isolate and disconnect from the rest of the world."*
>
> *Dr. Steve Arterburn*

Phase 1 of a Crisis—The Impact Phase

The first phase of a crisis is the impact phase. This phase:

1. *Hits suddenly and stuns*
   This phase lasts 24-36 hours.

   One of two responses are possible:
   - **Stay** and deal with it.
   - **Run** away from it.

   When you run from a crisis you **postpone the resolution**.

2. *Leaves the person numb and disoriented*
   These are all processes for handling the pain.
   - Do **not** expect much **rational thinking** at this time.
   - The person can **forget** and wander mentally.
   - There can be **denial** and a **search** for what has been lost.
     They will continue to search for what has been lost:
     "No, that isn't my son you found. It must have been someone else."

3. *Do not give advice at this time*

> *If you give them advice,*
> *they won't hear it, it won't register,*
> *and they will get angry at you.*

✎ What you do is accept the person's . . .

_____

- Draw out the feelings.
- Just be there.
- Sometimes you don't have to say anything.
- They need your presence.

4. *They will ask "Why?"*
During the impact phase the person will often ask the question "Why?" This is not a time to give answers.
- Instead, give them permission to ask why.
   "If I had experienced what you have experienced, I'd be crying out, 'Why?'"
- Give them permission to vent what is inside of them.

> *"In the midst of a crisis, the big question*
> *always comes up: Why? Why me? Why now?"*
>
> *Dr. Paul Faulkner*

5. *Give simple Scriptures*
Give only the simple Scriptures. They are not ready for complex theology. Remember their thinking is not functioning well.
- A passage that will give comfort.
- A passage reflecting emotion or anguish
- Not an extensive study

6. *Keep prayers simple*
Avoid complex prayers. Just use **simple prayers**.
- **Prayers that reflect** their feelings or their anger.
   "God we are just coming apart."
   "God we know your comfort is there, but we don't feel it."

• You don't have to know whether the prayer registers or not. The main thing is to **be there**.

> *You are not there to solve their problems—*
> *just to guide and to love them.*

Questions and Answers

Review

1. Memorize each of the following Counseling Fundamentals. Incorporate them in work with your practice journal.
   • *Teach and admonish*
   • *Be honest*
   • *Be accepting*

2. What is the best way to say difficult things when you must admonish someone?

3. How long does the impact phase last?

4. How does a person typically feel or react during this phase?

5. Why is it important for you to listen in this phase? Should you give them advice?

6. How should you handle the question: "Why?"

7. What is the proper use of prayer and Scripture during the impact phase of a crisis?

Teaching and Admonishing

One way to say a difficult thing to an individual is to use tentative statements (or "empathic leads") such as:

"Could it be that you're hurting yourself . . . ?"
"Have you ever considered what he would have done if . . . ?"
"Do you suppose that . . . ?"
"I really hear you saying that . . . "
"Do you really mean that . . . ?"

For more of these "empathic leads," see the appendix. In Session 5 we will have more discussion of empathic leads— phrases to start statements that show concern and also invite a response from the other individual.

Break into pairs and practice these types of phrases given the following situations.

1. A very self-conscious person believes that someone hates them.

2. A person who gossips too much is hysterical because someone has accused them of breaking a confidence.

3. A person is making threatening comments about someone who has hurt him/her. "I'll kill them!"

4. A woman is trying to get back at her husband by having an affair of her own.

5. A man has chosen an alternative lifestyle or is doing drugs and blames his parents,

6. A girl who is a very sloppy dresser is upset because someone has called her a "slob."

7. Add any of your own situations.

Being Honest

You are a counselor. The individual you are counseling asks you the following questions. To what extent must you be honest with the individual? Give examples of the types of things you could say.

1. Have you (the counselor) ever had an affair?

2. Do you think I'm wrong? (in a situation where the counselee is obviously wrong)

3. Why doesn't God love me?

4. Have you ever been angry at God?

5. Do you think they really hate me? (you know that they do hate him/her)

6. Why won't he marry me?

7. Am I fat?

8. Have you ever really wanted to kill somebody like that?

Being Accepting

1. What one thing could a counselee say that would shock you?

2. Did your family talk openly about difficult topics when you were growing up? Give an example.

3. Do you enjoy being around people who talk a great deal about their personal problems?

4. Is there some topic that's shocking by nature, but is an area that you've experienced in your life? Is it an area in which you would have a special ministry for counseling?

Personal Applications

Rate yourself on how well you apply the following in your daily life. (1 is poor/10 is excellent)

1. How good are you in dealing with situations where you have to admonish someone (tell them something they may not want to hear)?

   Poor   **Good**

   1   2   3   4   5   6   7   8   9   10

2. How do you respond when someone tells you you're wrong? Give a personal example.

3. Do you want people to tell you if you're wrong? How do you want them to tell you?
   How should a friend tell you?
   How about your boss?
   How should God tell you?

Summary and Prayers

1. What have you learned from this lesson?

   _____.

   _____.

   _____.

   _____.

2. Write your prayer list for this session and for the coming week.

_____ .

_____ .

_____ .

_____ .

_____ .

_____ .

_____ .

_____ .

> _Focus on simplicity—simple prayers,_
> _simple scripture._
> _We want people to remember the simplest of facts:_
> _that God loves them and God cares for them._

SESSION V

"Patterns of Pain"

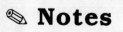 **Notes**

Patterns of Pain

Counseling Phases

> Look not every man on his own things,
> but every man also on the things of others.
> Philippians 2:4 (KJV)

In Session 4, we learned about the impact phase of a crisis. We learned that the impact phase hits suddenly. It's a time when the person is numb and disoriented. It's a time when you need to listen more than you need to give advice. It's a time when the person wants to ask, "Why?" which is a question you really shouldn't answer for them.

In Session 5, Dr. Wright covers the final three stages of a crisis. After the initial impact, the person tends to withdraw and be confused. From this confusion, we can help someone find an eternal perspective—God's perspective. Then there is growth and adjustment, and finally, a sense of hope.

As we learn the phases of a crisis, Dr. Wright stresses that there are no precise boundaries between the phases. Interpreting the phases can be very subjective, but within the limits of our judgment can be very useful—if not critical—in understanding how to minister and how to help.

Viewing the Video

Phase 2—Withdrawal and Confusion

After 24-36 hours a person in crisis moves to a time of emotion. In this phase, all the emotions can be present—depression, anger, ambiguity, uncertainty.

> *"It's extremely important to work through the grief process.
> . . . we do not grieve as those who have no hope—but indeed
> Christians do grieve and it's extremely healthy to do that."*
>
> *Dr. Frank Minirth*

1. *They don't know where to go*
    - They can try to **bargain**

          "Honey, if you come back to me I'll be faithful."
          "Lord, if I can keep the home, I'll pray every day."

    - Or they can try to **detach**

          "I don't want to go with her any more. She had problems."
          "I really didn't want that car."
          "It didn't matter."

    - They will start **asking** you what to do.

2. *Give them task-oriented direction*
    Offer several suggestions and let them choose.

          "When you've had difficulty before, what were some of the things that you did that worked for you?"
          "What do you think are some possibilities?"

3. *Throw away the clock*
    Do not limit the time you spend with an individual. Continue until the person has some "balance."

4. *Understand their feelings*
    - **Bewilderment**

          "I never felt this way before."

    - **Danger**

          "I feel so scared."
          "Something terrible is going to happen."

    - **Confusion**

          "I just can't think clearly."
          "My mind is so muddled it doesn't seem to work.

    - **Impasse**

          "I'm stuck."
          "Nothing I try seems to work."

    - **Desperation**

          "I've go to do something, but I don't know what to do."

    - **Apathy**

          "Nothing can help me."
          "What's the use? Why try?"

    - **Helplessness**

          "I can't cope by myself. Would you please help me?"

    - **Urgency**

          "Help me now. I can't wait."

    - **Discomfort**

          "I am so miserable and unhappy."

5. *Help them articulate their feelings*
   Use the above list of phrases as examples. Memorize these examples. Use phrases like these:
   > *"Do you have an apathetic feeling like nothing can help you?"*
   > *"Do you have a sense of confusion like you can't think clearly?"*

6. *Help them manage their painful feelings*
   The first way to do this is to help them identify those feelings.
   > *"Could you put into words what's going on."*

   - Make statements to **give them permission** to share their feelings
     > *"It's natural to feel anger . . ."*
     > *"You must be really upset . . ."*
     > *"It's so normal to be resentful . . ."*
     > *"It's important for you to express that anger that's inside you."*

   - Help them discover what their feelings mean to them.
   - They may share it in **offensive words**. What do you do?

   _____

   - Try writing a **journal**.

7. *Understand the potential negative effects of their feelings*
   - Depression
   - Suicide

   ✐ You always take any suicidal hint as_____.

   - Anger

8. *Find ways to help people deal with their feelings*
   - Exercise
   - Laughter
   - Take a break from dealing with the crisis
   - Put the feelings in perspective
   - One thing we can say:
     > *"In time these to will pass."*

Ministering to Those in Phase 1 and 2

1. *Listen*
   The most important thing you can do is listen. That's what friends are for—to be there and listen. Listening is like a gift of yourself and your time.

2. *Give reassurance*

Reassurance does not mean everything will turn out all right. Even if things are bad, you can still reassure them that:
- What they feel is normal.
- You will be there to help them.
- They will not be alone.
- God still loves them.

3. *Encourage*

Encouragement means believing in them. Give them a phone call. Focus on only the positive things.

4. *Reflect back what you hear them saying*

Encourage them to continue talking by repeating back in simple phrases and sentences the types of things they have said to you. It tells them you are really listening.

Phase 3—The Adjustment Phase

Phase 3 is a time of positive thoughts in the midst of all the negative thoughts. The person is more capable of solving problems. This is a time of searching for some new object to give meaning in life.

✎ Make sure they do not short-circuit the

_____

1. *A time of focused exploration.*
They can explore possibilities.
> *"You know, I think this might work."*
> *"Here's a way out of this."*
> *"Here's a possibility."*

The support they need from you is to continue to help them make decisions on their own.

2. *A time of spiritual insight*

✎ This phase can take . . .

_____

- Ask questions
  > *"What have you learned about God?*

"What do you think is going to be different in your life?"
"What is significant for you spiritually?"

- Use Scripture
- Use inspirational books

Help to build something spiritual into their life so that they can learn something for the next crisis. You can handle the crisis better the next time by what you learn now.

Phase 4—A Sense of Hope

✐   This phase will take

_____

1.   *A sense of hope*
     - Working hard on problems
     - Getting new insights

2.   *Reattachment to something new*
     This is a process of filling the vacuum.

3.   *A sense of reality testing*
     "These new discoveries I've made—are they really true, do they really work?"

4.   *What should you do?*
     - Reinforce the hope that they have.
     - Keep talking to them about:
       *"What have you **learned**?"*
       *"How will you handle crisis **differently** the next time?"*

Group Discussion

✐   How will I make use of the *Change and Crisis Sequence Chart* in ministering to other people? Refer to the Appendix for this chart.

_____

_____

_____

Ways to use the chart
- Plot where individuals are in a crises.
- Determine what to do and what not to do.
- Identify individuals stuck in Phases 1 or 2.
- Show to individuals their phase in a crisis.
- Learn the phases ahead of time.

> *It's not how much you know; it's how much you care.*
>
> *Dr. Gregg Weber*

Questions and Answers

Review

1. List typical behaviors of a person in Phase 3 of a crisis— the Withdrawal and Confusion Phase.

2. What types of feelings can a person have in this phase?

3. How do you deal with a person in this phase?

4. Memorize the main guidelines for dealing with a person in Phases 1 and 2.
   - *Listen*
   - *Give them reassurance*
   - *Encourage*
   - *Reflect back what you hear them saying*

5. Describe Phase 3— "The Adjustment Phase"

6. Describe Phase 4— "A Sense of Hope"

Dealing With Feelings

Following is a summary of some of the principles described by Dr. Wright for dealing with the feelings of individuals in Phases 1 and 2. Describe what is meant for each of the principles.

1. Give them task-oriented directions.

   _____ .

2. Throw away the clock.

   _____ .

3. Understand feelings in this phase.

   _____ .

4. Help them articulate their feelings.

   _____ .

5. Help them manage their painful feelings.

   _____ .

6. Understand the negative effects of feelings.

   _____ .

7. Find behaviors to help people deal with their feelings.

   _____ .

Identify the Feelings

Dr. Wright has identified 9 different feelings that are characteristic of Phase 3—the Withdrawal and Confusion Phase.

- bewilderment
- danger
- confusion
- impasse
- desperation
- apathy
- helplessness
- urgency
- discomfort

Identify an emotion that goes with each of the following statements. For some, more than one choice is possible.

1. "I can't think this through clearly." _____ .

2. "Nothing can help, so why try?" _____ .

3. "I have to get over this so I can get on with my life." _____ .

4. "I need to understand this now!" _____ .

6. "I can't sit still." _____.

7. "I just don't know what to do." _____.

8. "I don't know how I am going to get on with the rest of my life." _____.

9. "I just don't understand, it happened so fast." _____.

10. "Nothing is wrong, I'm just fine." _____.

11. "I feel so scared." _____.

12. "My mind is so muddled it doesn't seem to work. _____.

13. "Nothing I try seems to work." _____.

14. "I've got to do something, but I don't know what." _____.

15. "What's the use? Why try?" _____.

Phase 1, 2, 3 or 4?

In the following situations decide whether the individual is in Phase 1, Phase 2, Phase 3, or Phase 4. Remember that boundaries between the phases can be vague. There may be characteristics of more than one phase in each situation.

1. It looks like John and Mary will lose their home. They've been fighting constantly. She blames him for not providing. He hasn't known what to do with himself since he lost the job. Mary's been praying—praying hard—that God will let them keep the house. She just wants this one thing. John leaves the house early, saying he's job hunting, but he drives to the lake and parks there staring at the water for an hour or more before he goes to the store for a copy of the employment section and a few half-hearted phone calls.

2. Jennifer went to the movies last night with Susan. Jennifer hadn't gone out since Paul had broken the engagement. From almost the first scene, she just started crying. The movie wasn't particularly sad, but she cried anyway. I think it was the male lead with the same color eyes as Paul. Afterwards she said, "I didn't know how much I needed that cry. I've been keeping it

all inside, and suddenly it was there at the surface." It's such a relief.

3. She was hysterical. Calvin tried to talk to her but she just kept crying. When he talked about the baby she began to hyperventilate with deep wrenching sobs. There was a wild look in her eyes. She kept saying over and over, "Why me? Why this child? Why me?"

4. Ione started a garden for the first time in 20 years. She'd forgotten the feel of dirt, and plant sets, and whether she wanted the smaller cherry tomatoes or the "Big Berthas." But now with her hands in the rich loam, she forgot about John, and the retirement years they'd had—the good years—until his cancer. Now she just felt the sun, and the breeze blowing the scarf against her cheek, and her nostrils filled with the imagined smells and the dreams of canning tomatoes for her grandchildren next June.

5. I was blaming God. There had been such an emptiness. There seemed no point to it all. But I got to thinking last night that if there had been no accident, I wouldn't have met Jill. I think God was involved in that. But what can I do with myself now with legs that won't work? The insurance will pay for school. Maybe I should take one of those tests that show your employment aptitude.

6. He started screaming at them. Can you imagine Mr. Cool just losing it like that? They had put so much into the development of that proposal, that when the bad news came, he got the entire office together and started blaming this person for that and the other person for something else. He kept repeating over and over the problem with the financial projections and each time he blamed someone else for the mistake.

7. She had found a box and held it nestled in two outstretched hands as her father dug the hole. The outside had been colored with pink and purple crayons, and the words "Mr. Bird" had been printed on the side with a marker. Her mother had shown her how to shape the letters. She had kept the box under her bed all night, and she was crying when her father checked on her at three. But now, before the hole in the ground, she looked up at her father and said, "I'm glad there are birds, Daddy, and I'm even glad there are cats, and I'm glad there's a heaven where God can take care of all of us."

Goals and Prayers

1. What have you learned from this lesson?

    _____.

    _____.

    _____.

2. Write your prayer list for this session and for the coming week.

    _____.

    _____.

    _____.

    _____.

    _____.

    _____.

    _____.

    _____.

6

SESSION VI

"Nuggets of Truth"

✎ **Notes**

Nuggets of Truth

Principles for Counseling

> I have no greater joy than to hear
> that my children walk in truth.
> III John 4 (KJV)

In Session 2 we talked about listening. Now we look at the subject of listening again, but with the objective of learning specific listening skills.

Listening is so important in crisis care, and it's a skill we have to develop. Most of us know how to talk about ourselves, but when we minister to others, we put the self aside and focus on someone else.

Also in this session, Dr. Wright discusses positive things we can do to help with crisis recovery. What do people who handle crises well have in common? We can learn from them to strengthen ourselves and prepare others.

Viewing the Video

Basic Principles for Counseling

1. *Listening*

   We are really talking about penetrating listening—listening beyond what the person is saying. This type of listening taps into the roots of feelings.

2. *Paraphrasing*

   To paraphrase is to repeat back what a person has told you. This is to confirm what they have said and helps with understanding. It also allows you a way to actively participate in the listening.

3. *Reflecting back*

   Reflecting back is making a statement that determines how the other person felt about something.
   - Use **empathic response leads** (see the Appendix)

- Empathic leads are **tentative** statements.
- They are an opportunity to **verify** what has been said.
- They deal with **feelings**.
- They include words that are **auditory**, **visual**, and **kinesthetic** (for effective communication to different types of individuals).

  "I hear you saying that . . ."

  "So as you see it . . ."

  "The thing you feel most right now . . ."

> *"Should we speak when someone is in crisis,*
> *or should we just be there?*
> *There are times for both."*
>
> Dr. Frank Minirth

Dr. Wright suggests that you **practice** the empathic leads. A good method is to read them aloud once each day for a month.

> *"I want to recommend to every pastor to gather people*
> *who have had different experiences . . .*
> *and see whether they have the potential to be a friends*
> *committee [to be listeners]."*
>
> Dr. E.V. Hill

4. *Help the person talk concretely*
   Help them to talk about real problems rather than imagined.

5. *Remember they mix past, present and future together*
   They will tend to mix up past, present and future, and there can be lots of repetition. Let them talk, but gently bring them back to concrete issues.

   To help yourself when the repetition goes on and on is to:
   - Pray for an abundance of patience.
   - Give them permission to repeat it again. Say to yourself, "This is normal."

6. *Endeavor to ease some of the emotional stress of the moment*
   Do whatever you can to lower the emotional level.

7. *Deal with immediate issues*
    The individual may want to: (1) solve everything immediately, (2) worry about consequences, (3) worry about the future.
    - **Bring them back** to the immediate situation.
    - Your main goal is to **ease the emotional stress** of the moment.

8. *Generate possible solutions*
    In each of the following, you are asking the person to generate his or her own solutions.
    > *"What do you think we could do?"*
    > *"Can you think of things that you've done before?"*
    > *"What do you think about this . . ."*
    > *"What might happen if you do this . . ."*

9. *Break solutions into small steps*
    What are they going to do next? What will they do in the next few moments? Have them plan out their move step-by-step.

10. *Confront obstacles to the solution*
    Don't allow the negative to control good solutions. Overcome their objections. Convince them.

11. *Identify acceptable solutions*
    If they come up with solutions that don't work, guide them to ones that will.

12. *Make a contract for action*
    Make an agreement with the individual once they accept a solution.

13. *Put it in writing*
    This is so important, because they won't remember if they are in a time of high emotion. With something written, they can use it to keep a focus.

People who Survive a Crisis the Best

1. *Characteristics of survivors*
    - They had someone who stood by them.
    - They understood of the magnitude of the problem.
    - They overcome their guilt.
    - They have a reason to live.
    - They have a Biblical perspective on life.

> *Crises don't occur in isolation.*

2. *Families that DON'T cope well in a crisis*
    - They're unprepared for the unexpected.
    - They don't talk.
    - They blame one another.
    - They magnify the seriousness of the problem.

STOP **Group Discussion**

What potential crises do you foresee coming in your life?

_____

_____

How will you handle them differently having seen this video series?

_____

_____

3. *Characteristics of families that do cope well in a crisis*
    - They don't do the last 4 things.
    - They refuse to be bitter.
    - They live in the present.
    - They creatively manage their conflicts (learn to problem solve).
    - They give each other room to breathe.
    - They protect each other.

Men, watch out for_____.
Listen and reflect.
> *"Honey, do you just want me to listen?"*

Learning Scripture to share

The following Scripture passages are useful in dealing with individuals in crisis. Dr. Wright suggests that you memorize these. For more, there is a page of Scripture aids at the end of this section. The passages are from the King James Version. Use your own translation if you prefer.

He healeth the broken in heart and bindeth up their wounds. (Psalm 147:3)

Let your conversation be without covetousness; and be content with such things as ye have: for He hath said, I will never leave thee, nor forsake thee.
(Hebrews 13:5)

Which hope we have as an anchor of the soul, both sure and steadfast, and which entereth into that within the veil. (Hebrews 6:19)

Let not your heart be troubled; ye believe in God, believe also in me.
(John 14:1)

Fear thou not; for I am with thee: be not dismayed; for I am thy God: I will strengthen thee; yea, I will help thee; I will uphold thee with the right hand of my righteousness.
(Isaiah 41:10)

The eternal God is thy refuge, and underneath are the everlasting arms: and He shall thrust out the enemy from before thee; and shall say, destroy them. (Deuteronomy 33:27)

Be strong and of good courage, fear not, nor be afraid of them: for the Lord thy God, He it is that doth go with thee, He will not fail thee, nor forsake thee. (Deuteronomy 31:6)

Be careful for nothing; but in everything with prayer and supplication with thanksgiving let your requests be made known onto God. And the peace of God, which passeth all understanding, shall keep your hearts and minds through Jesus Christ. Finally, brethren, whatsoever things are true, whatsoever things are honest, whatsoever things are just, whatsoever things are pure, whatsoever things are lovely, whatsoever things are of good report; if there be any virtue, and if there be any praise, think on these things. Those things, which ye have both learned, and received, and heard, and seen in me, do: and the God of peace shall be with you. (Philippians 4:6-9)

Card-Carrying Worriers

For those who find themselves worrying too much. Take a note card or a calling card. Write the word STOP on one side and Philippians 4:6 on the back . Carry the card yourself as a reminder when you start to worry. Give cards to others if there is a need.

> *Be careful for nothing; but in everything by*
> *prayer and supplication with thanksgiving*
> *let your requests be made known unto God.*
> *Philippians 4:6*

Questions and Answers

Review

1. Review the 13 principles for counseling in this session. Memorize them. Describe what each of them means.

2. What factors allow individuals to survive crises well?

3. What factors allow families to survive crises well?

Group Exercises—Role Playing

Break into groups and develop role-playing situations that practice the listening skills described in this session. One person acts as the individual in crisis, another as the care giver. The rest of the group observes (this can also be done in pairs without the larger groups). The role players must be creative and add to the script and situation.

Steps for group role playing are as follows:
1. Break the solutions down step-by-step.
2. Identify acceptable solutions—acceptable and comfortable for them.
3. Repeat and paraphrase the solutions back to the person in crisis.
4. Write the solutions down.
5. Ask for the next contact—"Call me tomorrow at . . ."

Practice following **all of these steps**. It's important to practice using the ideal format, so you will have confidence in the real situation.

Use your **listening skills**: paraphrase, reflect back, help the person talk concretely, focus on what you can solve immediately, generate possible solutions.

Use **empathic response leads** as needed. There was practice for these kinds of responses at the end of Session 4 (see "Teaching and Admonishing"). Refer to the list of empathic responses in the Appendix.

1. Use a problem you're having in your own life. Keep it simple—pick a light problem to start.

2. You are a mother or father who has just lost an infant child.

3. Your teenage daughter informs you she is pregnant and wants an abortion. A friend of hers has already set up an appointment.

4. You have just had an automobile accident in a friend's car. You are safe, but the car is a wreck.

5. You have learned that you have cancer (breast cancer, ovarian cancer, or colon cancer).

6. Your spouse has just told you he/she is leaving you for someone else. Apparently there is a homosexual relationship involved.

7. Think of the worst possible situation you could be in (within the limits of good taste) and act that situation out. Use your imagination.

8. Situations of your choice _____.

_____.

_____.

_____.

Round-Robin Role Playing

Another way to develop a role-playing situation is to pass the dialog along. You may have seen the type of game where one person starts a story with a sentence; then the second person has to continue the story by adding a sentence, then the third person, and the fourth, etc. It's passed around, with each participant making up his/her creative element.

Do this same type of exercise, but with the objective of learning crisis-care skills.

One person in a group acts as the central care giver, but the role of counselee is passed from person to person. Each participant has to pick up from where the last counselee left off. The care-giver uses an empathic lead sentence between each participant to bind the script together.

Who Survives a Crisis and Who Doesn't

Some of the people in the following situations are handling crises well and some are not. Why do they handle it the way they do? How can you help?

1. Susan lost her father after a long struggle with Leukemia. She seems overcome with guilt and has shut herself off from friends. Susan's mother, who was the primary caretaker of her father during his sickness, tried to visit Susan yesterday after church to bring her some fresh cut flowers.

2. Sally's teenage son was killed by a drunk driver. She's thrown herself into working with an activist group opposed to drunk driving. It's almost become an obsession with her. Sally's husband works late at the office since the accident. He wants nothing to do with his wife's activities.

3. Mike's wife, Anne, left him and the children suddenly and without any reason apparent to Mike. Neither Mike nor Anne will talk to each other. Their two teenage kids had been discipline problems at school and they feel they are to blame. Mike spends a lot of time with the children. He tries to dedicate a specific amount of time each week to each child. He's joined a singles group at a new church.

4. Amy was not chosen cheerleader captain. Her mother has taken her out of school for a few days to "recuperate." Her father feels they are overreacting. The parents fought openly about the situation in front of Amy last night. Amy's friend on the cheerleader squad called her and they talked for two hours, Her friend knew why she hadn't been selected, but she decided not to say anything to Amy about it. She mainly just listened.

5. Donna and Robert are having marriage difficulties. Both of their families seem to be constantly interfering. Donna and Robert both use their families as allies in attacking one another. Donna's friend Jim took Robert aside last night and told him to "grow up." Robert was furious. Carol, who knows them both very well, took Donna to lunch yesterday and tried to get her to talk about it, but Donna got mad at her.

Scripture for Sharing

Following are Bible passages that Dr. Wright suggested for use in care situations. Look up each of these and write them out. Memorize them.

* Psalm 147:3_____.

* Hebrews 13:5_____.

* Hebrews 6:19_____.

* John 14:1_____.

* Isaiah 41:10_____.

* Deuteronomy 33:27_____.

* Deuteronomy 31:6_____.

* Philippians 4:6-9_____.

For additional passages, refer to the list in the Appendix.

Rating Yourself

Dr. Wright identified the following factors for individuals who tend to be successful in handling crises. How do you rate?

		Poor				Good
1.	Had another person who stood by them.	1	2	3	4	5
2.	Understood the magnitude of what happened.	1	2	3	4	5
3.	Overcame their guilt.	1	2	3	4	5
4.	Had a reason to live.	1	2	3	4	5
5.	Had a Biblical perspective on life.	1	2	3	4	5

What single change could improve your ratings?

_____.

_____.

_____.

_____.

_____.

Rating Your Family

Dr. Wright identified the following factors in families that are successful in handling crises. How do your family members rate?

	Poor				Good
• Prepared for the unexpected.	1	2	3	4	5
• Do not hurt one another by staying silent.	1	2	3	4	5
• Do not blame one another.	1	2	3	4	5
• Do not magnify the seriousness of problems.	1	2	3	4	5
• Refuse to be bitter.	1	2	3	4	5
• Live in the present.	1	2	3	4	5
• Creatively manage their conflicts (learn to problem solve).	1	2	3	4	5
• Give each other room to breathe.	1	2	3	4	5
• Protect one another.	1	2	3	4	5

What single change could improve your family's ratings?

_____ .

_____ .

_____ .

_____ .

Goals and Prayers

1. What have you learned from this lesson?

_____ .

_____ .

_____ .

_____ .

_____ .

_____ .

_____ .

2. Write your prayer list for this session and for the coming week.

_____.

_____.

_____.

_____.

_____.

_____.

_____.

_____.

_____.

✎ Notes

Grace Products

SESSION VII

"Hope for the Hurting"

Notes

Session 7

Hope for the Hurting

Depression

> He healeth the broken in heart,
> and bindeth up their wounds.
> Psalms 147:3 (KJV)

"I'm depressed!" What does that mean? It can mean anything from not feeling very well to having a dangerous diagnosed clinical condition. What is depression? Dr. Wright talks about depression and sadness in this session. Next time he will talk about loss and grief. All of these are dimensions of the feelings and conditions that affect us when bad things happen.

Can a Christian be depressed? Some people say no. There's an idea that if God is in your life, then the negative can't be in your life. In fact, Christians and non-Christians experience many of the same problems, but Christians have a relationship with God to bring them through those problems.

Dr. Wright talks here of a number of excellent techniques for dealing with individuals in depression. Of course, a person in serious depression needs professional care. But as a first contact, as a friend, as a Christian church member, you can be there caring and listening.

Viewing the Video

What is Depression?

Almost everyone has experienced depression. We will have opportunities to deal with people who are depressed. What do we do and say? Unfortunately, there is a lot of misinformation about depression.

 Group Discussion

✎ If Romans 8:28 is true, how can a Christian become depressed?

> *Depression is nothing more than a message system telling us that something else in our life is going haywire, and we need to listen to the message and deal with it.*

 Is it a sin for a Christian to be depressed? _____.

> *"When my faith is shaken, frequently what I'm doing is getting my eyes off Jesus Christ and getting my eyes on men.*
> *. . . There is someone who will never, ever fail you, and that's Jesus Christ."*
>
> *Dr. Gene Getz*

Depression vs. Sadness

Both depression and sadness can significantly affect a person, but depression is a particularly intense reaction to problems, loss and/or crisis.

- Depression is more intense than sadness
- Depression lasts longer
- Depression interferes in a significant way with day-to-day functions

> *And he took with him Peter and the two sons of Zebedee and began to be sorrowful and very heavy.*
> *Then saith he unto them, My soul is exceeding sorrowful, even unto death; tarry ye here and watch with me.*
> *Matthew 26:37-38 (KJV)*

Characteristics of Depression

What are some of the main characteristics of depression. How can we recognize depression?

1. Hopelessness

2. Despair

3. *Apathy*

4. *A loss of perspective*
    Problems become large in the mind of the person. There is an emphasis on the negative.

5. *A change in physical activity*
    There can be a change in sexual behavior—typically less. There can be eating disorders or changes in eating patterns—too much or too little. The person sleeps too much or not enough.

6. *A loss of self-esteem*

7. *They cut themselves off from others*
    The person withdraws or stays away from activities. "There's nothing worthwhile in life." There may be a desire to escape from life.

8. *They consider suicide*
    Suicide is always important to consider in a case involving depression. Any mention of suicide should be taken seriously and there should be immediate referral to a professional.

    ✐ Who are most prone to take their life by suicide?
       A. teenagers B. men C. elderly men D. elderly women E. divorced men

    _____

    To answer this, note the following groups have the highest risk of suicide (that is, suicide that is completed).
    *   The group that uses the most violent methods
    *   The group that lacks a social network
    *   The group that struggles with physical limits

9. *They're oversensitive*
    Statements such as these are typical.
    > *"They don't like me."*
    > *"They're just asking me to church because they feel obligated."*
    > *"I know they don't want me around."*

Catch Depression in the Early Stages

It's best to catch depression in the early stages. Recognize the ways that depression can develop.

1. *Sudden depression*

   This is a depression that develops over some unplanned crisis and set of events.

2. *Gradual development of depression*

   Sometimes depression can develop slowly over a long period of time, sometimes with little awareness on the part of the individual.

3. *Spiritual reactions*

   Watch for sudden changes in a person's attitudes toward God.

It's important that we keep our perspective
in the midst of a crisis . . .
If we gather around us supportive Christians;
if we get the counseling that we need;
and we determine to persevere with the Lord . . .
We'll get through it if we don't lose perspective.

Dr. Steve Arterburn

Causes of Depression

There are many things that can lead to depression, but the following are some of the more common.

1. *Insufficient food or rest*
2. *Medications*
3. *Physical causes*
4. *Reproductive problems*
5. *Repressed anger*
6. *Loss (grief depression)*
7. *Negative thoughts*
8. *Faulty behavior—guilt*
9. *Success*

> *"You need to grieve.*
> *Grieving is a time of letting go.*
> *If we don't let go of the loss, we will increase*
> *the level of our depression that we'll carry through*
> *the rest of our lives."*
>
> *Dr. Steve Arterburn*

The Five R's—A Guide for Remembering How to Help

1. *The first R is* _____.
   Have empathy for the person. Let them feel comfortable

2. *The second R is* _____.
   Have them talk about the depression. Have them answer questions.
   > *"How long have you felt this way?"*
   > *"When do you remember this starting?"*
   > *"What happened to bring this on?"*
   > *"Do you feel depressed all the time or only periodically?"*
   > *"If you don't feel depressed all the time, how long does the depression last?"*
   > *"When does the depression occur?*
   > *"Do you ever get help?"*
   > *"Now that you're depressed, what's the next step to go ahead?"*
   > *"What are the options you have to handle this depression?"*
   > *"What's the worst thing you imagine happening because you're depressed?*

3. *The third R is* _____.
   Give them reassurance that you'll be there to help them, reassurance that in time the depression can lift.

> *If you're questioning whether*
> *your belief is strong enough,*
> *it's not the amount of your belief;*
> *it's the one that you believe in.*
>
> *Dr. Frank Minirth*

- One type of reassurance is to give them detailed structure
- Work on **behavior first**

  "It's easier to change a depressed person's behavior than their thought life."

4. *The fourth R is* _____.

   Help them to learn things they didn't know before—to do things differently.

5. *The fifth R is* _____.

   Help them to reorganize their life—to be different than they were before they were depressed.

Basic Guidelines in Working with Depression

1. *Understand the causes and symptoms of the depression*

2. *Watch for suicidal behavior*

   Take any mention of suicide seriously and make a referral.

3. *Encourage the person to see a doctor*

   Encourage the person to have a complete physical if it appears necessary.

4. *Support them*

   Give them full support. Get family members involved in support. Tell family members not to avoid the loved one who is depressed, and accept the fact that the person is in pain.

5. *Empathize*

   Use empathy rather than sympathy. Empathy is "walking with them."

6. *Help them with eating and sleeping*

   Help them solve any eating or sleeping problems.

7. *Suggest activities*

   These are activities to break the pattern of the depression.

8. *Don't make jokes*

   You must not try to joke or tease them out of a depression.

9. *Don't lecture*

   Remember it's how much you care, not how much you know.

Grace Products

10. Encourage

Here is one way to say it:

> *"Perhaps you can't do some of the things the way you used to. I understand that. But why don't we talk about the things you are able to do and what we can learn together?"*

Questions and Answers

Review

1. Is it a sin for a Christian to be depressed? It all right?

2. What is the difference between depression and sadness?

3. Memorize the following characteristics of depression
   - *Hopelessness*
   - *Despair*
   - *Apathy*
   - *Loss of perspective*
   - *Change in level of physical activity*
   - *Loss of self-esteem*
   - *Being cut off from other people*
   - *Potential for suicide*
   - *Oversensitivity*

4. What are some of the main causes of depression?

5. What are the five R's?

6. Memorize the key words in bold in the following list of ways to help with depression.
   - **Understand** *the causes and symptoms of the depression*
   - *Watch for* **suicidal** *behavior*
   - *Encourage the person to* **see a doctor**
   - **Support them**
   - **Empathize**
   - *Help them with* **eating or sleeping problems**
   - **Suggest activities** *to break the pattern of the depression*
   - **Don't make jokes** *about them or tease them*
   - **Don't lecture**
   - **Encourage**

Depression vs. Sadness

In the following situations, decide whether the person is depressed or sad. Tell what you would say to the person.

1. Sarah was fired from her job last week. She hasn't stopped crying, has slept very little, and has made herself ill.

2. Your son's football team lost the state championship by one touchdown. He's been moping around the house for the last two days.

3. John has experienced 5 rejections from women in the past year. He seems to have become a shell of his former self.

4. Ruth gives you her favorite painting, and then promises more of her prized artwork. You know she's been having a lot of problems lately, and that she hasn't been handling them well.

5. Amy's boyfriend is in the hospital after a car accident. She seems to be handling the crisis, but lately she's been expressing feelings of guilt.

Causes of Depression

Following are some causes of depression noted by Dr. Wright.

- *Insufficient food or rest*
- *Low blood sugar*
- *Feminine problems*
- *Repressed anger*
- *Loss (grief depression)*
- *Negative thoughts*
- *Faulty behavior—guilt*
- *Success*

Choose the three, in your opinion, that are the most important. Discuss this with your group.

1. _____.

2. _____.

3. _____.

The Five R's

Give your own definitions to each of the following keys to helping someone in depression.

1. Rapport _____.

2. Relief _____.

3. Reassurance _____.

4. Revelation _____.

5. Reorganization _____.

Guidelines in Working with Depression

In each of the following situations, critique how the person handles the situation. In each situation it is the care giver who is thinking or speaking. What is done right and what is done wrong? Which of the guidelines in the list below is applicable?

- *Understand* the causes and symptoms of the depression
- Watch for *suicidal* behavior
- Encourage the person to *see a doctor*
- *Support them*
- *Empathize*
- Help them with *eating or sleeping problems*
- *Suggest activities* to break the pattern of the depression
- *Don't make jokes* about them or tease them
- *Don't lecture*
- *Encourage*

1. He just seems angry all the time. I wonder if there is something wrong at home? I think I'll ask him to talk about his family or perhaps his work. Maybe if I can just get him talking about anything, he'll say some things I can ask him to explain further.

   _____.

2. He's really hurting. He's being an absolute jerk about it, but underneath you can tell there is a lot of pain. (empathize)

   _____.

3. He's been complaining about his back the entire time. No matter what we talk about, he mentions his back. And I feel uneasy when he says that life isn't worth living with that kind of pain. It looks like he's a body builder, so his physical shape must be important. I told him he needs to see a doctor.

   _____.

4. She kept carrying on and on, so I tried teasing her a little to see if I could shock her out of it. I thought if she could laugh at herself, it would be a good sign. Good laughs are good medicine.

   _____.

5. "Well, I told him he just needed to grow up. I said, "If you had half an ounce of sense you'd know that you've had

an attitude about that job for months. You've been talking like a two-year old. If I was your boss . . ."

_____ .

6. "You say you're feeling like it's your fault. I can't make you stop feeling that way. I'd probably feel that way myself. But when I look at you standing there all I can think about are the times you were strong for me. You're really a wonderful person. You wouldn't do anything to hurt anyone, not on purpose."

_____ .

7. "Come on. Let's go get some snacks. I'm sure people will be stopping by and you'll have something to offer them. Besides it will give us something to do. You've been cooped up here too long. Let's get your car keys, and I'll help you check the pantry."

_____ .

8. "Mary, I'm worried. It's been 2 months and you've been eating and eating, and you're skinny as a rail. You need to see Dr. Nelson. I'm serious. Can I call and make an appointment?"

_____ .

9. "Bob, your mother is not doing well. I know she calls you and says she's fine, but I'm here. I see her every day, and I'm worried. Why don't you come down this weekend. Get some of the kids to come over and check up on her."

_____ .

10. "I don't care what you've done. I'm here and I'm going to listen. You're the most important thing to me right now."

_____ .

Personal Applications

1. Have you ever experienced depression? Describe that experience.

2. How could someone have recognized your depression? What behaviors did you exhibit?

3. What could someone have done to help you during the depression?

4. What are your favorite Bible verses when you're depressed or sad?

5. Where is God when you're depressed?

Summary and Prayers

1. What have you learned from this lesson?

_____.

_____.

_____.

_____.

2. Write your prayer list for this session and for the coming week.

_____.

_____.

_____.

_____.

_____.

_____.

_____.

_____.

_____.

Because God Loves Me

Because God loves me He is slow to lose patience with me.

Because God loves me He takes the circumstances of my life and uses them in a constructive way for my growth.

Because God loves me He does not treat me as an object to be possessed and manipulated.

Because God loves me He has no need to impress me with how great and powerful He is because He is God, nor does He belittle me as His child in order to show me how important He is.

Because God loves me He is for me. He wants to see me mature and develop in his love.

Because God loves me He does not send down His wrath on every little mistake I make, of which there are many.

Because God loves me He does not keep score of all my sins and then beat me over the head with them whenever He gets the chance.

Because God loves me He is deeply grieved when I do not walk in the ways that please Him, because He sees this as evidence that I don't trust Him and love Him as I should.

Because God loves me He rejoices when I experience His power and strength and stand up under the pressures of life for His name's sake.

Because God loves me He keeps on working patiently with me even when I feel like giving up and can't see why He doesn't give up with me too.

Because God loves me He keeps on trusting me when at times I don't even trust myself.

Because God loves me He never says there is no hope for me; rather, He patiently works with me, loves me and disciplines me in such a way that it is hard for me to understand the depth of His concern for me.

Because God loves me He never forsakes me, though many of my friends might.

Because God loves me He stands with me when I have reached the rock bottom of despair, when I see the real me and compare that with His righteousness, holiness, beauty, and love. It is at a moment like this that I can really believe that God loves me.

Yes, the greatest of all gifts is God's perfect love.

Grace Products

SESSION VIII

"Expect the Unexpected"

 **Notes**

Session 8

Expect the Unexpected

Loss: Part 1

> Wait on the Lord: be of good courage,
> and he shall strengthen thine heart.
> Psalms 27:14 (KJV)

The next two sessions are about changes and about loss. There is an old saying: "Everything always changes." From those changes we sometimes gain and we sometimes lose. It can be like a roller coaster—rise and fall, gain and loss, rise and fall.

Loss is so much a part of life. Loss is unavoidable, but we can choose our reaction to loss. We can choose bitterness and anger; or we can choose to grow. We can choose to use our experiences to deepen character and increase in our understanding of God.

In this session, Dr. Wright tells us how to deal with losses in our life and in the lives of others. He explains 4 types of loss—real, abstract, imagined or threatened. He will also share with us about the value of loss.

Viewing the Video

What is a Loss?

As Dr. Wright discusses types of losses and gives examples, write down any that appear appropriate to your situation.

_____

_____

_____

_____

_____

> *If you don't recognize something as a loss,*
> *then you don't spend time and energy*
> *dealing with it and grieving over it,*
> *and it's captured inside of you just waiting*
> *for the next loss to occur.*
> *Then it really impacts you.*

Types of Losses

1. *Real or concrete loss*

   For example, a person, a car, a broken heirloom. This is the loss of something tangible.

2. *Abstract loss*

   For example, love, hope, ambition, control. This is a loss that's difficult to measure, but real.

3. *Imagined loss*

   Thoughts of loss that may not have happened. For example, imagined rejection, second-guessing people's motives.

4. *Threatened loss*

   For example, threatened job loss, waiting for the worst on a medical report. These are difficult to measure, but they are real.

   ✐ Which is the most difficult loss to handle?

   _____

> *"Trials can teach us sensitivity.*
> *They can deepen our compassion level.*
> *They can increase our patience,*
> *and they can even give us more genuine love,*
> *if we'll trust God . . ."*
>
> Dr. John Trent

Group Discussion

If loss is the root cause of a sense of depression or grief, it's important to identify that loss. The following questions by Dr. Wright can be used to draw information from a person and have them share and identify losses: Use these in your groups to answer the question:

What was one of the earliest significant losses in your life?

One person indicates they have a loss to share. The other group members draw it out with questions. Use the questions that are appropriate, and make up questions as needed. Ask the questions in love and concern. Take time to listen, and use your listening skills.

- *When did this loss happen?*
- *How old were you?*
- *Where was it?*
- *What were your feelings at the time?*

The Purpose of Loss

Is there value to loss? When a loss occurs, it's normal to ask the question: "Why?" As we look for the answer, we learn new things about ourselves and God.

1. *Loss teaches us that we can't have what we want every time.*
   We live in a world that demands immediate satisfaction. Losses change and fortify our beliefs.

2. *Loss is an opportunity to experience the comfort of God.*
   God is there for us if we will be open to him.

> *"Whatever the pain that we go through in life,
> God can use that to equip us for ministry to other people."*
>
> *Dr. Carl Brecheen*

3. *Loss teaches us to depend on God.*
   Many times our lives appear to be falling apart. But God is there for us. We can discover the extent of the comfort of God.

Correct Responses to Loss

At some point in a loss the question "Why?" can change to a set of new questions:

1. *What can we learn through this experience?*
2. *How can we grow through this experience?*
3. *How can God be glorified through this experience?*

The lessons may not be immediate. Do not expect an individual to come to the realization of the value of a loss immediately. They must first walk through the dark period.

> *"Grief has been my companion and has taught me much."*
>
> *Dr. H. Norman Wright*

Losses in your life

 Is there any other loss in your life that you haven't grieved over?

_____

_____

_____

> *We recover from loss by learning to grieve.*

STOP Group Discussion

 How would you describe grief? Make a list

Grief is: _____.

Grief is: _____.

Grief is: _____.

Grief is: _____.

Grace Products

Grief is: _____.

Grief is: _____.

Grief is: _____.

What is Grief?

✏ Grief is _____ _____ _____ caused by loss, disaster, or misfortune.

- Grief is sorrow and deep sadness.
- Grief comes from the Latin root word "to burden."
- Mourning is the process of expressing the sorrow from grief.

Don't Bury your feelings

- There is a myth that says you should bury your feelings.
    "Don't share your feelings"
    "You'll upset people by acting that way."
- You need to release your feelings.
- When you're in grief, you'll be ambushed by feelings.

Questions and Answers

Review

1. What is a loss?

2. Describe four types of losses.

3. What value do losses have in our lives?

4. What is grief?

5. Why is it important to share your feelings?

Four Types of Loss

In each of the following situations, identify the type of loss.
- *real*
- *abstract*
- *imagined*
- *threatened*

1. _____ Death in the family.

2. _____ Demotion at work.

3. _____ Hearing noises at night.

4. _____ A lack of desire at work.

5. _____ Tornado warning in area.

6. _____ Husband has an affair.

7. _____ Doctor finds a lump.

8. _____ Friend moves away.

9. _____ An alien spaceship might come.

10. _____ Your car is broken into.

11. _____ Your home burns down.

12. _____ Layoff rumor at work.

13. _____ Possibly being drafted in wartime.

14. _____ Unsure of boss's reaction to a presentation.

15. _____ An individual has bad visions from drug use.

16. _____ It sounds like a rodent under the house.

Good from Loss

Sometimes good can come from loss. Identify the "good" that can come from each of the following situations.

1. Your child is leaving for college in the morning.

2. Amy's father passes away after a long bout with cancer.

3. Your son's best friend becomes involved with drugs.

4. John discovers he's contracted the AIDS virus.

5. Nobody likes a new supervisor at the office.

6. Bill's girlfriend has just broken up with him.

7. Robert is forced to declare bankruptcy after his small business folds.

8. Tom gets "cold feet" at his own wedding. The ceremony is postponed.

9. Beth's husband leaves her with their two children.

10. Jack loses the City Council election.

The Power of Positive Thinking

Dr. Wright suggests the following exercise for overcoming loss or depression.

A.   Write down 5 events that you know will give you pleasure.

B.   After each write down 2 or 3 pleasant thoughts about the event.

C.   Transcribe these on a card, and every hour or two during a time of grief, take out the card and remember the pleasant things.

1) _____.

2) _____.

3) _____.

4) _____.

5) _____.

The Treasure Within

Read 2 Corinthians 4:7-18. Have members in your group read from different translations. Answer the following:

1. Describe the "treasure" that we have within us. (vs. 7)

2. While that treasure is within us, what is happening around us? (vs. 8-9)

3. Explain the meaning of verse 10.

4. In vs. 16-17, why does he never become discouraged?

5. What is the difference between the seen and unseen? What are the seen and unseen? (vs. 18)

6. How have you used the treasure within you when you have experienced grief?

Personal Applications

1. In your life, what crisis has caused you to grieve the most?

2. Have you ever been "ambushed" by feelings, as described by Dr. Wright? Tell about that time.

3. Is there a loss that you have not fully grieved over? How can the experience help you to care for others in their grieving?

Summary and Prayers

1. What have you learned from this lesson?

   _____.

   _____.

2. Write your prayer list for this session and for the coming week.

   _____.

   _____.

   _____.

   _____.

   _____.

   _____.

   _____.

Grace Products

SESSION IX

"Exploding the Myths"

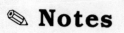 **Notes**

Exploding the Myths

Loss: Part 2

> The Lord is my strength and my shield:
> my heart trusted in Him, and I am helped . . .
> Psalms 28:7 (KJV)

This is part two in our series about loss. In the last session we learned that loss comes from changes in life. We learned about different types of loss and that loss can have value.

The topic in this session is recovery from loss. This is the grieving process. Dr. Wright tells us some common myths about helping people who grieve. These are well meaning reactions and perceptions, but they typically do not help. Instead, Dr. Wright provides a list of suggestions for what to do and how to behave around someone in the grieving process.

You do not want to be a "miserable comforter"—someone who only makes the situation worse. Dr. Wright gives practical suggestions to be a wiser counsel and friend.

Viewing the Video

Common Myths About Loss

Myth 1—Replace the loss as soon as possible.
> *"Oh, go find a new girlfriend. There's plenty of fish in the sea."*
> *"Don't cry about it, let's go down to the pet store and we'll buy you something new."*
- Allow a person **time to grieve**—to acknowledge the loss.
- **Affirm their feelings** and have them talk about the loss.
- When they are ready, then talk to them about replacement.

Myth 2—Grieve by Yourself
> *"Don't affect other people. You're going to upset them."*
> *"Why don't you just stay home for awhile until you get better?"*
- This is contrary to what works.

✐ What works is_____.

- People need to talk about their situations.
- People need to have their friends check on them and be concerned.

Myth 3—Time heals all wounds
> *"Give it time, it'll be okay."*

- After a crisis settles, friends tend to draw back from the subject.
- Support can be needed months or years after a loss.

The 3-Month Follow-Up

People need time to grieve, often long after others have resolved the issue or have moved on to new problems. Thus it is most important as a crisis counselor to remember the problems and individuals involved at regular intervals.

1. *Keep a record on a calendar.*
2. *Every three months contact the individual.*
3. *Contact by phone, letter or personal visit*
4. *Remember anniversary dates unique to the situation.*
    It may be good to chart these on the Intensity of Grief Chart in the Appendix.

Average Times of Grief

To emphasize the need to follow-up, note the following average times of grief in the case of death:

1. *Death through natural causes*   _____ *years.*
2. *Accidental death*   _____ *years.*
3. *Suicide*   _____ *years.*
4. *Homicide*   _____ *years.*
5. *The death of a child*
    (the ultimate bereavement)   _____.

> *"Be there. Just show up!*
> *. . . Don't try to say anything deep or profound.*
> *Let them know that you care.*
> *Let them know that you love them.*
> *Pray with them and pray for them.*
> *Listen. Ask questions."*
>
> *Dr. Gary Oliver*

Unhealthy Manifestations of Grieving

Look for the following danger signs in dealing with individuals in crisis situations.

1.	*Suppression of emotions*	An individual hides his/her emotions. "Oh, they are being so brave."
2.	*Extended indecisiveness*	Over a long period of time an individual has trouble making decisions.
3.	*Behavior detrimental to the person's best interest*	The individual gives his/her possessions away.
4.	*Self punishment because of guilt*	"Oh, if only I had done this!"
5.	*Apparent insensitivity to a loss*	Feelings and emotions are hidden behind a facade.
6.	*Hyperactivity*	Some individuals avoid mourning by staying busy—too busy.
7.	*Enshrinement*	Setting aside the room of a loved one and keeping it just as it was.
8.	*Altered relationships*	The individual becomes a recluse or drinking becomes a problem

Expressions Of Grief

When we grieve, there are three common messages given. When you grieve:

1. *You express your* _____.

2. *You express your* _____.

3. *You express the* _____ *of the experience.*

All of these are normal. As a crisis counselor we need to help individuals with this type of expression.

How Do We Help Someone Recover From a Loss?

1. *Help them identify the loss*

 Group Discussion

In Session 8, there was group discussion to help identify losses from the past and whether they have been fully grieved over. Repeat this exercise now to allow more individuals to participate and to deepen the group dynamics.

A person volunteers that they have a loss that they still grieve about. The other group members draw it out with questions.

- *When did this loss happen?*
- *How old were you?*
- *Where was it?*
- *What were your feelings at the time?*
- *How long did you feel this way?*
- *What happened to change your mood?*
- *Have you ever experienced these feelings again? When?*
- *When did (do) these feelings tend to occur? In the morning, evening, night, weekdays, weekend, holidays, etc.? Were you in a particular place? With someone else? Who?*
- *What did (do) you do when those feelings came?*
- *Did that loss change your life?*
- *What are the options you have had for handling that change?*

2. *Help them change their relationship with what was lost*
   - You can never recover what has been lost.
   - You have the memories, but not the reality.
   - Develop acceptance of the changes that will come

3. *Help them find new ways to function*
   - Functioning without the thing they have lost.
   - For many this will involve a new identity, particularly for spouses.

4. *Help them replace the emotional investment*
   - Every relationship has an emotional investment.
   - You do move on in life, but in the midst of the crisis, you don't believe it.

> *"Who is the therapist's counselor?*
> *It's my friends.*
> *It's my prayer group."*
>
> *Dr. Paul Faulkner*

Practical recovery steps

1. *Be sensitive to what the other person needs*
   Do not project onto the other person what we think they need.
   > *"Should I just listen?"*

   We are not experts on other people. With our children we have the tendency to want to give them advice all the time. Do we really listen to them?

2. *Try to identify what does not make sense about the loss*
   "Why now, why me?" Identify the feelings.

3. *Treat the feelings like a guest*
   Guests only stay for a time, and then they leave.

4. *What steps or actions do you need to take to overcome the loss*
   Get people to talk to you and share with you about their loss. If you hear the person talk to you about the same thing week after week, that's the time to give them a gentle nudge

5. *Measure the intensity of their grieving*

   From week to week there may be a feeling by the person that nothing is changing—their sorrow never lifts. Have them write down the intensity of their feelings and chart the intensity through time. Show them their pattern of intensity after a period of time to emphasize that there has been a change. Teach new criteria of growth in recovery.

6. *Focus on the strengths in a person's life*

   Get them into the Psalms. When they pray, encourage them to express hopes and prayers for the future. Ask the person "Where do you want to be two years from now? Let's dream."

   > *"One of the things that we need to do in the midst of every difficulty of life, is stop long enough to see the good things that are happening and have happened.*
   > *. . . Life is good because God is with us."*
   >
   > Dr. Carl Brecheen

7. *Tell about the stages of grief*

   Many people do not know how to grieve. Teach them the 5 stages of grief. Emphasize the stages are normal and necessary.

8. *Say good-bye*

   The biggest thing in any loss is saying good-bye. They must acknowledge they are no longer going to share this life with certain individuals.

9. *Write letters*

   Express the things they wish they had expressed before. Write things out as though the individual that is gone would read what is written.

   > *"It's hard to say good-bye. . .*
   > *I think we just have to ask God to heal our wounds.*
   > *Sometimes we have to write some letters. . .*
   > *As we ask God to heal our hearts from saying good-bye,*
   > *we lower our expectations, bring them back to reality,*
   > *and then we can experience healing."*
   >
   > Dr. Steve Arterburn

Questions and Answers

Review

1. Describe 3 common myths people have about loss?

2. What is the 3-month follow-up?

3. Describe each of the following manifestations of grieving:
   - *Suppression of emotions*
   - *Extended indecisiveness*
   - *Behavior detrimental to self*
   - *Self punishment from guilt*
   - *Insensitivity to loss*
   - *Hyperactivity*
   - *Enshrinement*
   - *Altered relationships*

4. How can we help people recover from a loss?

5. Describe 9 practical recovery steps. (see below)

Spotting the Myths

What is the flaw in each of the following statements made by well meaning people? Note the three myths discussed by Dr. Wright in this session.
   - *Replace the loss as soon as possible..*
   - *Grieve by yourself..*
   - *Time will take care of it..*

1. Oh, Bobby, you're upsetting your sister with all that talk about that old dead dog. Just hush up. We'll get another dog. There are plenty at the shelter.

2. She so strong. She stood by the graveside and didn't cry once. I'm so proud of her.

3. You're crying like a baby, Mary, and everyone is sick of it. Why don't you go to your room and close the door?

4. Don't worry, you'll forget about him. "There's more than one fish in the sea."

5. You're just having one of those mid-life crises. If you just stopped talking about that nonsense, you'd probably get over it.

7. Computer jobs are a dime a dozen! Check the employment section on Sunday and you'll have a new one by the middle of the week.

Healthy or Not?

Which of the following is a healthy behavior and which is not? For help, check the section "Unhealthy Manifestations of Grieving"on page 97. Some of these may be healthy under some conditions but not others. Explore the possibilities.

1. Suppressing emotions
2. Avoiding memories
3. Feeling the need to say good-bye
4. Having apparent insensitivity
5. Wanting to talk through a problem
6. Continued indecisiveness
7. Expressing feelings
8. Expressing feeling months after a crisis
9. Talking about effects from experiences
10. Self-punishment
11. Crying
12. Exhibiting self-destructive behavior
13. Hyperactivity
14. Protesting what has happened in a crisis
15. Altering relationships

Practical Recovery

Take the most recent crisis in which you have been involved. It may have been your crisis or someone else's. Which of the following steps to recovery would have been helpful in that situation? Describe how it could have been implemented.

1. Being sensitive to what the other person needs

2. Trying to identify what does not make sense about the loss

3. Treating the feelings like a guest

4. Determining steps or actions to overcome the loss

5. Measuring the intensity of their grieving

Grace Products

4. Determining steps or actions to overcome the loss

5. Measuring the intensity of their grieving

6. Focusing on the strengths in a person's life

7. Telling about the stages of grief

8. Saying good-by

9. Writing letters

Summary and Prayers

1. What have you learned from this lesson?

_____.

_____.

_____.

_____.

2. Write your prayer list for this session and for the coming week.

_____.

_____.

_____.

_____.

_____.

_____.

_____.

_____.

✎ Notes

SESSION X

"Silence is Golden"

✎ Notes

Session 10

Silence is Golden

What to Say

> Hear, O Lord, when I cry with my voice:
> have mercy also upon me, and answer me.
> Psalms 27:7 (KJV)

In Session 1 of this series, the first question posed was "What's the right thing to say, the right thing to do in a crisis? Well, we've come full circle, because with the background we've had on crisis and loss, we're now ready to talk about what to say. This builds on everything we've learned.

This is a session of comparisons and contrasts. Dr. Wright deals with specific situations and specific statements that can help or hurt. We learn words that can hurt and words that can encourage.

A major theme through this series has been how to listen. Before we can speak, we have to know how to listen. We've learned how to listen to others. In this session we learn how to listen to ourselves.

Viewing the Video

Situations

Here is a sampling of some of the good and not so good things that can be said in various situations.

1. *At the time of a funeral*

    What not to say:
    > "He's so much better off in heaven."
    > "If there's anything I can do, call."

    What to say instead:
    > "I'm always going to remember him because of the times we had together."
    > "I'm going to come by with dinner tonight."

    *   **Be personal** about your own remembrances.
    *   **Be specific** about how you will help.
    *   **Reflect the loss** back to the person.

2.   *At the death of a baby*

What not to say:

"You can always have another one."

"Be thankful you have Jenny."

"At least you never got to know it."

What to say instead:

"I know how much being a mother means to you."

"This must be devastating for you."

3.   *During a divorce*

What not to say:

"You know I never liked the way he treated you anyway."

"There are two sides to every story."

What to say instead:

"The future must seem frightening."

"I'm going to be available to you at all times."

"I'm sure this is a lonely time for you. Let's get together for lunch on Tuesday. How would that be for you?"

4.   *Placing an elderly parent in a rest home*

What not to say:

"How in the world could you put your own mother in such a place."

What to say instead:

"I know how much you love her and I'm sure you're doing the best thing for her."

5.   *When a pet dies*

What not to say:

"Hey, it's only a dog."

"You can always buy a new kitten."

What to say instead:

"I know that this pet was really important to your family."

6.   *Terminal illness*

What not to say:

"I know a lady who had the same thing. She lived 4 months after they told her."

"Won't you be glad to be with the Lord?"

What to say instead:

"How are you feeling about what you're facing?"

"I'd like to take you to your next doctor's appointment and be there with you."

> *"Tools such as empathy, of caring, of listening, of being there,*
> *of being present, sometimes of not even saying anything.*
> *Those are the tools and resources that . . .*
> *I've seen God use to soften hearts, to bring hope,*
> *to transform people."*
>
> Dr. Gary Oliver

What to Say/What Not to Say

1. *Do be personal*
   Be personal about your own remembrances.

2. *Do be specific*
   Be specific about how you will help.

3. *Do reflect the loss*
   Reflect the loss back to the person.

4. *Don't minimize their pain*
   What not to say:
   > *"It's probably for the best."*
   > *"Things could be worse."*
   > *"You're young. You can get over it."*

5. *Do acknowledge their loss*
   Offer simple understanding statements.
   > *"I feel for you during this difficult time."*
   > *"This must be very hard for you."*
   > *"I share your feelings of loss."*
   > *"I wish I could take the hurt away."*

6. *Don't say, "I'm so sorry."*
   It's hard to respond to "I'm so sorry."
   Instead, **add something** to "I'm Sorry."
   > *"I'm so sorry. I know how special this person was to you."*
   > *"I'm so sorry. I'm going to miss them as well."*
   > *"I'm so sorry. I'm really going to make myself available for you."*
   > *"I'm so sorry. Is there something I can pray about?"*

> *"God is not interested simply in working with perfect people.*
> *He's interested in working with broken people*
> *who can appreciate the contribution of His grace*
> *and His power in solving the problems,*
> *the realistic problems of their lives."*
>
> Dr. Howard Hendricks

7. *Do offer to do something specific*

   Don't say, "Is there anything I can do?"

   This places the burden on the person in crisis—They have to find answers.

   Ask yourself, "What would I need—If I were in a similar situation?"

   Then, **be specific** about what you can offer:

   > *"I'm on the way to the store. What can I pick up for you?"*
   > *"Would tomorrow be a good day to come and help clean the house?"*
   > *"Would your children like to come over and play this afternoon?"*

8. *Don't say, "You shouldn't feel that way."*

   We're the judge—This places us in the position of being the expert.

   Instead, encourage the person to **express their feelings**.

   Suggest they write their feelings out.

   Suggest they keep a journal.

9. *Don't try to answer their question: "Why?"*

   We don't have an answer.

   Instead, you can say the following:

   > *"I don't know why. I wish I did. I know you wished you had an answer."*
   > *"I wish I had an answer to give to you."*
   > *"It's okay to ask the question. Ask it again and again."*

   Do not say:

   > *"If you were a Christian you wouldn't have a need to ask why."*

10. *Don't Offer Spiritual Answers*

    Don't offer spiritual answers to the question: "Why?".

    > *"You're going to be a stronger person."*
    > *"You'll really find the meaning in this."*

   ✏ That's part of being a_____.

   We don't know . . . Why this has happened.

        Grace Products

We don't know . . . Why some people go through traumas and others not.
We don't know . . . The Scripture that's needed. The lessons they'll learn.

11. *Don't Put a Timetable on Recovery*

Don't say:

> *"Everybody goes through this stage at this time, etc. . .*

Instead, when showing a chart, emphasize:

> *"This is the average."*

Allow them the time that they need to deal effectively with all the phases of their grief.

12. *Don't Quote Numerous Bible Verses.*

There may be a proper time for Scripture, but . . .

God may lead you to a verse, but . . .

    . . . As a general rule don't quote numerous Bible verses.

In particular, don't quote Bible verses as a way to minimize their feelings.
Instead, **give spiritual encouragement from your heart**.

    Use passages that bring comfort.

    Use passages that have comforted you.

> *"During a time of crisis,*
> *the most effective thing that you can do,*
> *the most effective thing that you can say, quite frankly,*
> *is to express and communicate your love."*
>
> *Dr. Gary Oliver*
>
> *"When you look at the person of Jesus, you see it all.*
> *He was the Master Counselor. . .*
> *To walk with the Master is*
> *to have the love of the Master."*
>
> *Dr. Paul Falkner*

---

13. *Do Respect Their Privacy*

Ask the person if you can put their name on a prayer chain.

Do not tell others without the person's permission.

Do not tell "horror stories" about others.

Instead, you can say:

"I would like to be able to understand."

"I haven't been through this so it's hard for me to comprehend how devastating this must be for you."

"I've never gone through that kind of a loss. My losses have been different, so I understand the pain of loss, but I really don't fully understand this."

A few simple statements can make a world of difference.

You may never fully comprehend how important your comments may be to other people

---

Questions and Answers

Review

What is the problem with each of the following actions and statements?

1. Minimizing pain_____.

2. "I'm sorry."_____.

3. "Is there anything I can do?"_____.

4. "You shouldn't feel that way!"_____.

5. Answering the question why_____.

6. Offering spiritual answers_____.

7. Putting a timetable on recovery_____.

8. Quoting numerous Bible verses._____.

9. Not respecting privacy_____.

10. "I Understand."_____.

What to Say

You are talking with a person in crisis. You catch yourself making one of the following statements. Take a deep breath and think. What should you say or do instead?

1. Minimizing pain—*"Things could be worse."*

   _____.

2. Saying you're sorry— *"I'm so sorry!"*

   _____.

3. Offering help— *"What would you like me to do?"*

   _____.

4. Telling them how to feel— *"You shouldn't feel that way!"*

   _____.

5. Asking why— *"If you had listened to me in the first place, you wouldn't have to ask why now."*

   _____.

6. Offering spiritual answers— *"God will make you a stronger person."*

   _____.

7. Placing a timetable on recovery— *"Give it a week and you'll forget about him."*

   _____.

8. Saying you understand— *"I know exactly what you're going through."*

   _____.

What do You Say . . .

What are some of the things you can say in each of the following situations. Review the answers suggested in the first part of this session.

1. To the widow or widower at the time of a funeral?

2. To the person sitting next to you at the funeral who is crying?

3. To your friend who has just had a divorce?

4. To your friend's spouse who initiated the divorce?

5. To a friend who is placing her father in a nursing facility because she wants to start a new career?

6. To the father who is going into the nursing facility?

7. To a small boy who has lost a pet lizard?

8. To an adult who has lost a pet dog?

9. To a women who has learned that her father has terminal cancer?

10. To the father who has the cancer?

Personal Applications

1. Rate yourself on your ability to find just the right words.

	Poor				Good
	1	2	3	4	5

2. What do you need to improve your rating?

3. Share within your group the techniques that the group members use for finding the right words.

4. Share some "bloopers" in your life—things you've said or were said to you. (Be careful with this one.)

Summary and Prayers

1. What have you learned from this lesson?

   _____.

2. Write your prayer list for this session and for the coming week.

   _____.

   _____.

3. For a special Bible exercise for the week memorize Romans 8:28. Write down situations in your daily life in which you were able to use this verse.

Grace Products

SESSION XI

"The Rubber Meets the Road"

 **Notes**

The Rubber Meets the Road

Case Studies: Part 1

> In thee, O Lord, do I trust; let me never be ashamed:
> deliver me in Thy righteousness.
> Psalm 31:1 (KJV)

In this session and in the following sessions a number of case situations are presented. These are designed for you to practice your counseling skills. You'll have the privilege of leading someone out of despair and into the light of God's love.

Play the tape, and after each situation is presented, stop the tape and discuss the approach to handling that crisis. Answer the questions provided and add your own questions as you prefer.

These participants are not actors. They are real people dealing with real crises and real loss.

Viewing the Video

Case Study Questions

The following questions can be used for group discussions in each of the case studies. These draw on principles learned in this series. In addition, there are specific questions asked for each case.

1. *Is this person experiencing a crisis or a loss?*

2. *What type?*

3. *What should you tell this person to do?*

4. *How is the individual responding to the situation? As a threat? As a loss? As a challenge?*

5. *If it were possible to talk to this individual, what types of questions would you ask?*

6. Identify the phase that you believe this individual is going through.

7. If you were able to repeat back this person's feeling using an empathic lead, what would you say?

8. Chart the individual's position on the Change in Crisis Sequence Chart. What guidance is needed at this point?

9. Chart where the individual might be on the Intensity/Duration Grief Chart. What holidays or times do you, as a counselor, need to pay special attention to for this person?

10. Does this person exhibit characteristics of someone who can cope/not cope with this situation?

11. Can you tell if this person is depressed or simply sad?

12. What are some Scripture references you might use in this situation? When is the most appropriate time to share them?

13. Is there an average time of grief in this situation?

14. Are you able to identify with this person/situation? How can that help/hurt your counsel?

15. Is there or will there be closure in this situation?

Case Study 1—Divorce— "Monte"

Play the video and stop when indicated. Then discuss the following in your group.

1. How do you deal with someone who is facing the loneliness of divorce?

   _____

   _____

   _____

2. How could you help a parent and/or children in this situation?

   _____

   _____

   _____

Case Study 2—Injury— "Pat"

1. *How do you handle this problem of the injury? Of the job loss?*

    _____

    _____

    _____

2. *How can you help ease the long-term physical pain?*

    _____

    _____

    _____

3. *She stated that she would be "a vegetable." How do you deal with this?*

    _____

    _____

    _____

Case Study 3—Miscarriage— "Thomas and Elfreda"

1. *What can you say or do for this couple who never had the chance to love and care for this child because of miscarriage?*

    _____

    _____

    _____

2. *How could you ease their fears as they try to have a second child?*

    _____

    _____

    _____

Case Study 4—Unjust Lawsuit— "Jamie"

1. *How can you help this person deal with the anger towards others who are blaming her unjustly?*

    _____

    _____

    _____

2. *How do you help her deal with the question of Christian values during this lawsuit?*

    _____

    _____

    _____

Summary and Prayer

1. What have you learned from this lesson?

    _____.

    _____.

2. Write your prayer list for this session and for the coming week.

    _____.

    _____.

    _____.

    _____.

    _____.

    _____.

    _____.

Grace Products

SESSION XII

"Making a Difference"

 **Notes**

Making a Difference

Case Studies: Part 2

> For our heart shall rejoice in Him,
> because we have trusted in His holy name.
> Psalm 33:21 (KJV)

In this session, as in last week's session a number of case situations are presented. These are designed for you to practice your counseling skills.

Play the tape, and after each situation is presented, stop the tape and discuss the approach to handling that crisis. Answer the questions provided and add your own questions as you prefer.

These participants are not actors. They are real people dealing with real crises and real loss.

Viewing the Video

Case Study Questions

As with Session 11, the following questions draw on principles used in this series, and can be used for group discussions. In addition, there are specific questions asked for each case.

1. *Is this person experiencing a crisis or a loss?*

2. *What type?*

3. *What should you tell this person to do?*

4. *How is the individual responding to the situation? As a threat? As a loss? As a challenge?*

5. *If it were possible to talk to this individual, what types of questions would you ask?*

6. *Identify the phase that you believe this individual is going through.*

7. If you were able to repeat back this person's feeling using an empathic lead, what would you say?

8. Chart the individual's position on the Change in Crisis Sequence Chart. What guidance is needed at this point?

9. Chart where the individual might be on the Intensity/Duration Grief Chart. What holidays or times do you, as a counselor, need to pay special attention to for this person?

10. Does this person exhibit characteristics of someone who can cope/not cope with this situation?

11. Can you tell if this person is depressed or simply sad?

12. What are some Scripture references you might use in this situation? When is the most appropriate time to share them?

13. Is there an average time of grief in this situation?

14. Are you able to identify with this person/situation? How can that help/hurt your counsel?

15. Is there or will there be closure in this situation?

Case Study 1—Disabling Illness— "Phil"

Play the video and stop when indicated. Then discuss the following in your group.

1. How do you comfort this man preparing for a major operation?

   _____

   _____

   _____

2. How could you help his spouse or child in this situation?

   _____

   _____

   _____

Case Study 2—Family Member with Cancer— "Harold"

1. *What can be done to ease the pain of this person who has lost a family member due to a terminal illness?*

_____

_____

_____

2. *How could you help this person complete the grieving process?*

_____

_____

_____

Case Study 3—Job Loss— "Dwight"

1. *How do you help this man? How do you help the family regain its security?*

_____

_____

_____

2. *What can you say or do to comfort the spouse in this situation?*

_____

_____

_____

Case Study 4—Death of a Child— "Dick and Carol"

1. *What are other ways you could help this person "chip away at the grief?"*

_____

_____

_____

2. Comment on the phases of grief this couple experienced? How did she describe her initial reaction?

_____

_____

_____

Summary and Prayer

1. What have you learned from this lesson?

    _____.

    _____.

2. Write your prayer list for this session and for the coming week.

    _____.

    _____.

    _____.

    _____.

    _____.

    _____.

    _____.

Grace Products

13

SESSION XIII

"I See That Hand"

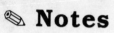 **Notes**

I See that Hand

Question and Answer

> For thou art my rock and my fortress;
> therefore for thy name's sake lead me, and guide me.
> Psalm 31:3 (KJV)

As you have followed along in this series, you have undoubtedly had questions. In this session, Dr. Wright answers questions from the audience. You may stop the tape at any point and discuss the audience responses. These questions are added as an enrichment and recap session for the series.

Some of these questions match questions available for group discussion in previous units. Compare your answers with those of Dr. Wright.

Personal Applications

Has this series helped you or someone you counseled? Do you have a success story to share with Dr. Wright? Please write him in care of the producer, Grace Products Corporation 1761 International Pkwy., Richardson, Texas, 75081.

It is our prayer that you have been equipped to better understand loss and crisis and to know what to say and what to do to minister to others.

May God bless you as you seek to care for those in crisis.

Viewing the Video

The Questions and Answers

1. *How do you deal with the loss of a child?*

_____

_____

2. What differences are there between Men and Women in terms of grieving?

   _____

   _____

3. How do you minister to a man who has lost a spouse through divorce?

   _____

   _____

4. How do you deal with a man who has lost his wife through death and will not grieve openly? What can a son (or daughter) do?

   _____

   _____

5. How does a church start a lay counseling training program?

   _____

   _____

6. What can be done for a crisis in an office? How can members of a professional group help a colleague who is grieving?

   _____

   _____

7. What do you say if you have said something that should not have been said?

   _____

   _____

8. How can one prepare for the time when family members may pass away?

   _____

   _____

9. If a person is grieving and you have had a similar loss or have experienced a similar crisis, how much of your own story do you relate?

   _____

   _____

Grace Products

10. What types of materials are available to minister to those who have had a divorce?

_____

_____

11. How does a church member inform his church body that they are not meeting a need, without alienating the church leadership?

_____

_____

12. How do we help someone to stop blaming God for their losses?

_____

_____

Summary and Prayer

1. What have you learned from this lesson?

_____.

_____.

2. Write your prayer list for this session and for the coming week.

_____.

_____.

_____.

_____.

_____.

_____.

_____.

Grace Products

✎ Notes

Appendix

Change and Crisis Sequence Chart

	Phase 1 Impact	Phase 2 Withdrawal Confusion	Phase 3 Adjustment	Phase 4 Reconstruction Reconciliation

Emotional Level

Time	Hours	Days	Weeks	Months
Response	Fight-Flight	Anger, fear, guilt, rage	Positive thoughts begin	Hope
Thought	Numbness, disorientation	Ambiguity, uncertainty	Problem solving	Consolidation of problem solving
Direction	Search for lost object	Bargaining, detachment	Search for new object	Reattachment
Search Behavior	Reminiscence	Perplexed scanning	Focused exploration	Reality testing
Guidance needed	Acceptance of feeling	Task-oriented direction	Support, spiritual insight	Breakthrough, reinforce hope

Adapted from H. Norman Wright, *Crisis Counseling* (Ventura California: Regal Books)and from a similar chart by Ralph Hirschowitz in "Addendum," a special feature of the Levinson Letter (Cambridge: The Levinson Institute, n.d.), p. 4.

Empathic Response Leads

- "You're kind of feeling . . ."
- "As I get it, you felt that . . ."
- "If I'm hearing you correctly . . ."
- "I sort of hear you saying that maybe you . . ."
- "The thing you feel most right now . . ."
- "So as you see it . . ."
- "As I get it, you're saying . . ."
- "I somehow sense that maybe you feel . . ."
- "I really hear you saying that . . ."
- "You're sort of feeling . . ."
- "I'm picking up that you . . ."
- "To me it's almost like you're saying, 'I . . ."
- "It kind of makes (made) you feel that . . ."
- "So, you feel . . ."
- "What I hear you saying is . . ."
- "What I guess I'm hearing is . . ."
- "You feel . . ."
- "I wonder if you're expressing a concern that . . ."
- "It sounds as if you're indicating . . ."

- "I wonder if you're saying . . ."
- "I'm not sure I'm with you, but . . ."
- "You place a high value on . . ."
- "It seems to you . . ."
- "Like right now . . ."
- "You often feel . . ."
- "You feel perhaps . . ."
- "You appear to be feeling . . ."
- "It appears to you . . ."
- "As I hear it, you . . ."
- "So, from where you sit . . ."
- "Your feeling now is that . . ."
- "I read you as . . ."
- "Sometimes you . . ."
- "You must have felt . . ."
- "I sense that you're feeling . . ."
- "Very much feeling . . ."
- "Your message seems to be, 'I . . ."
- "You appear . . ."
- "Listening to you it seems as if . . ."
- "I gather . . ."
- "So your world is a place where you . . ."
- "You communicate (convey) a sense of . . ."

Help from Scripture

Comfort

Psalm 46:7	Isaiah 41:17	Deuteronomy 31:6	Psalm 94:14
Numbers 14:9	Psalm 103:17		Psalm 27:10
Psalm 73:23		Matthew 28:20	John 6:37-39

Peace

Romans 5:1,2	Exodus 33:14	Psalm 85:8	Proverbs 16:7
Psalm 119:165	Isaiah 26:3	Isaiah 57:2	
Isaiah 32:17	Matthew 11:29	Ephesians	
Colossians 3:15	John 14:27	Numbers 6:24-26	

Fear

Hebrews 13:6	Joel 3:16	Psalm 28:7	Deuteronomy 1:17
Jeremiah 15:20	Deuteronomy 7:21	Psalm 4:8	Psalm 56:3
Isaiah 35:4	Isaiah 41:10	1 Chronicles 16:25.26	
Nehemiah 4:14	2 Corinthians 1:10	Philippians 4:9	

Anxiety

Matthew 11:28	Proverbs 3:5,6	Psalm 86:7	Psalm 50:15
Job 34:12	John 16:33	Isaiah 40:11	Isaiah 41:13
Psalm 55:22	Psalm 20:7	Genesis 28:15	Psalm 68:19

For Those Who Feel Weak

Psalm 142:3	Ephesians 3:16	Psalm 55:18	Psalm 62:11
Habakkuk 3:19	Psalm 147:6	2 Corinthians 12:9	Jeremiah 10:6
Psalm 72:13	1 Chronicles 16:11	Isaiah 57:15	

Despair

Haggai 2:4	Ezekiel 34:16	Psalm 100:5	Psalm 199:116
Isaiah 40:29	Daniel 2:23	Hebrews 10:35	
James 1:12	2 Thessalonians 3:3	Psalm 46:1	
Isaiah 51:6	Ephesians 1:18	Jeremiah 32:17	

Grief

Isaiah 43:2	Psalm 116:15	Revelation 21:3,4
Psalm 71:20,21	Psalm 119:28	Psalm 119:76
Psalm 119:50	2 Corinthians 1:3,4	2 Thess. 2:16,17

Times of Trouble

Psalm 50:15	John 16:33	Psalm 138:7
Psalm 9:12	Psalm 37:39,40	Psalm 121:5-8
Psalm 46:1	Psalm 138:7	Psalm 34:7

Feeling Desperate and Depressed

Zephaniah 3:17	Psalm 42:11	Psalm 34:18	Psalm 40:1,2
Psalm 30:5	John 10:10	Psalm 126:5	

Intensity Grief/Duration Chart

This chart shows the patterns through time of the Intensity of Grief . Note the jagged peaks. Grief comes and goes in cycles. In a crisis, pain and grief build to an intensity at three months and then gradually subside, but not steadily. There are numerous ups and downs. The three-month landmark is important for a counselor. Make a note on your calendar to contact a person you are helping again after 3 months.

Also, note the intensity peak at the one-year anniversary. Most people don't need a reminder of this anniversary if it involves the loss of a loved one. The intensity of grief comes rushing in with pain that rivals the initial feelings of loss. You may want to avoid reminding the person of the loss at this time, but you can be sensitive to the person's needs as they share with you. This is certainly not a time to ever tell a person that they should be "over it by now" or "feeling better."

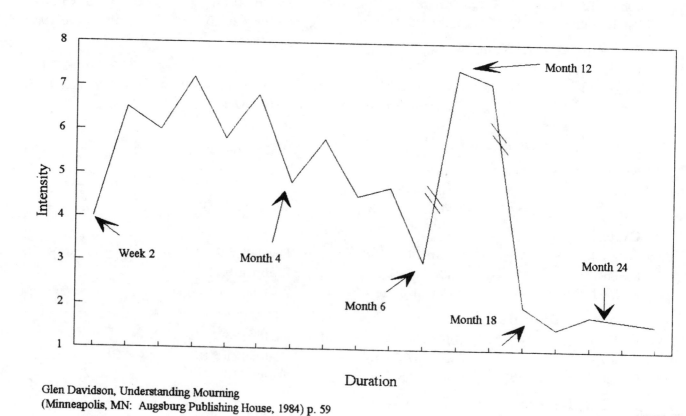

Glen Davidson, Understanding Mourning
(Minneapolis, MN: Augsburg Publishing House, 1984) p. 59

Grace Products